Jackie Womack

He Drew Her Body to His.

'Stop! What's the reason for this?'
demanded w   rom
Scott's passio   ?'

'Very sane,' S   grimly.
that I can see   after—what's going
on in your mind.'

'What I'm after?' Her brow furrowed in
confusion. 'Would you mind explaining?'

'Don't play innocent with me,' he rasped. 'I'm
not in the mood for it. In fact, it's a very
different mood I happen to be in. . . .'

ANNE HAMPSON
currently makes her home in England, but this
top romance author has travelled all over the
world. This variety of experience is reflected in
her books, which present the ever-changing
face of romance as it is found wherever people
fall in love.

Dear Reader:

I'd like to take this opportunity to thank you for all your support and encouragement of Silhouette Romances.

Many of you write in regularly, telling us what you like best about Silhouette, which authors are your favorites. This is a tremendous help to us as we strive to publish the best contemporary romances possible.

All the romances from Silhouette Books are for you, so enjoy this book and the many stories to come. I hope you'll continue to share your thoughts with us, and invite you to write to us at the address below:

Karen Solem
Editor-in-Chief
Silhouette Books
P.O. Box 769
New York, N.Y. 10019

ANNE HAMPSON
Dreamtime

Silhouette Romance

Published by Silhouette Books New York

America's Publisher of Contemporary Romance

SILHOUETTE BOOKS, a Simon & Schuster Division of
GULF & WESTERN CORPORATION
1230 Avenue of the Americas, New York, N.Y. 10020

ISBN: 0-671-57202-4

First Silhouette Books printing February, 1983

10 9 8 7 6 5 4 3 2 1

Chapter One

The sensible thing to do, thought Jane as she allowed her pensive gaze to rest on the rugged face of Paddy Haig, was to get right away, at this early stage, before something drastic happened.

Margaret was a home help in the Australian Out-back, on a massive station where thousands upon thousands of cattle roamed the wide spinifex plains. And Margaret was coming home to marry the boy she left behind just over a year ago.

'I went because I wasn't sure of my feelings for Doug,' she had written recently to Jane, her friend from schooldays. 'But now I know that my heart really wants Doug. But this life out here, Jane, is

7

great, so why don't you take over my job? I can speak to the Boss, who doesn't want to lose me and so will readily agree to having someone recommended by me. Jacana Downs is one of the three largest cattle stations in the whole of the Northern Territory and you'd love working here. Think about it and let me know not later than the end of the month as I shall be returning to England about five weeks from now.'

'What's the cause of that frowning expression, love?'

Jane had seen Mary approaching—Mary who was engaged to Paddy. She adored him, and it had seemed he had eyes for no one else . . . until he met Jane. . . .

'I was deep in thought,' answered Jane with a forced little smile. 'Margaret's written to say she's coming home and thinks I could have her job if I wanted it.'

'Her job—out there in the wilds?' It was Mary's turn to frown. 'You'd not like that, Jane.'

'Oh, I don't know. It would be a change from the office stool and a temperamental boss.'

'Don't go,' persuasively. 'You're part of the crowd and we'd all miss you, just as we missed Margaret when she left.'

At that moment Paddy came up so Jane was spared the problem of finding a suitable answer.

'Our dance, Jane,' he said lightly and swung her into his arms. 'It's a nice party, isn't it?' His face was close; Jane stiffened and tried to move a little.

'Very good. Bill's dad must be richer than we

thought to give his son a twenty-first like this. The Princess is the most expensive hotel in town.'

'I know.' A small pause and then, 'It's warm in here, Jane. Let's go outside for a while. I like the gardens here.'

She stiffened again, and thought of Margaret's letter.

'I don't find it warm,' she said.

'Jane. . . . This situation—'

'I don't want to dance any more,' she broke in sharply. 'I feel like having something from the buffet table.' She tried to pull away but his arm was strong about her. 'You're engaged to Mary,' she reminded him in the same sharp tone of voice.

'Only engaged, not married,' he returned and there was a sigh in his voice.

'I'm hungry,' she insisted. 'I'm not dancing any more.'

He had no option than to let her go; she walked swiftly to the long buffet table and found herself beside Margaret's sister, Josie, who said at once that she too had heard from Margaret.

'She's coming home and am I glad! I've missed her, as you know.'

'She said she could get me her job.' Jane was frowning as she helped herself to smoked salmon. To have to go away, so many miles, simply because of the danger facing her and Paddy. That Paddy was fast falling in love with her was evident; as for Jane's own feelings—well, she had determinedly fought his attraction but knew all the time that she was merely shirking the danger. Mary was far too sweet to be hurt and she, Jane, had not the slightest intention of causing her pain.

'She did?' Josie stood away to look at Jane, the fork idle in her hand. 'What's her idea, I wonder?'

'She knows I'm not very happy with my job here, for one thing. Also, when she was going I did say I envied her the adventure.'

'Will you consider going out there, to that god-forsaken wilderness?' Josie's gaze was sceptical. It was plain that she was assuming Jane to have more sense than to do what Margaret had done.

'I am considering it,' was Jane's frank response. 'It could be fun.'

'Fun!' Josie grimaced and added, 'I rather think you're joking.'

'It would be different.'

'Not different in the way you'd enjoy,' stated Josie in firm decisive tones.

'The experience would add to my education.' Jane took a roll and pat of butter and put them beside the salmon. 'I'm of the opinion that I shall let Margaret apply for the job for me.' It's the only sensible solution to my problem, she added to herself as Paddy's large frame came into her line of vision.

She flew to Brisbane where she caught a train for Goulalong in accordance with Margaret's instructions.

'At Goulalong you'll be met by a man called Lanky and his wife, Sue. The Boss wouldn't send Lanky on his own as he thought you'd be nervous, camping out with a complete stranger, so he's having Sue come as well. Sue and Lanky are living in one of the bungalows I told you about but you of course will be living in the main house.' Margaret had added more details about the homestead which was a Georgian-style mansion set on a slight rise overlooking its own well-tended grounds. 'The MacDonnell Ranges form the only diversion in a landscape of endless miles of grazing grounds. I hope you'll not become bored, Jane. I soon found that one has to be fairly self-sufficient out here, in what they call the 'Never-Never'. I ride, and swim in the pool; I take part in all the 'home-made' entertainments like gymkhanas, shed dances and film shows. Despite the great distances between the stations we do manage to arrange parties—get-togethers where we meet all the far-flung neighbours, some homely like ourselves and others who put on airs, conscious all the time of their status as great landowners, members of the great squatocracy, the very elite of whom Scott Farnham is one of the 'top-notchers'! He's arrogant, and some! Devastatingly good-looking in a tough, Tarzan kind of way! Bronzed and virile! A superb horseman, swims like a fish in his massive pool; dances too, which surprised me because at first glance one would think he was far too superior to take part in the more popular pastimes. He has a girl-friend—daughter of Francis Woolcott, owner of Dermot Waters, the ranch adjoining ours. She's as superior and arrogant as the Boss and they'll match to perfection. No love match, I'd say, but they'll get along for all that. Can't imagine either of them ever falling in love. The Boss is thirty now and still dallying but it has been rumoured recently that Daphne Woolcott is pushing for an engagement and I reckon the Boss will agree because of the profit involved. Daphne is the only child of Francis and his wife, Laura, so Dermot Waters will eventually be the prize—or compensation!—for the Boss taking on a girl whom many of us don't care much for. I shall look forward with interest to your opinion of her. You're rather more than pretty so it could be on the cards that she'll be jealous, so watch it! She never can bear for Scott even to look at another woman.'

Jane's thoughts wandered on as she sat comfortably in her seat and stared at the countryside racing past her. The train had passed through the Great Divide before entering the vast terrain of brigalow scrub and acacias—monotonous scenery and yet already Jane was sensing something which was attractive, which created a strange and unfathomable excitement spinning about in her veins. An adventure! And what would it bring? She had told Margaret she would come for a year initially and, if she liked the life, she would stay on indefinitely. She was looking forward to it even though she had been warned by Margaret that not only was the work hard but that the Boss was a stickler for perfection.

'Do something wrong and you're for it,' Margaret wrote. 'His tongue can lash in spite of that rather attractive Australian drawl that invariably softens a man's voice. He'll not spare you if you are ever so unwise as to displease him.'

Jane had grimaced at that, and decided there and then to watch her step with this god-like creature who appeared to rule his vast estate with the magisterial attitude of a feudal lord in the times of Medieval England.

The scenery changed and temperate grasslands predominated for a while. The railway station was reached at long last and it was with a sort of renewed energy that Jane rose from her seat as the train came to a halt.

The couple were there—Lanky, as his nickname implied, being tall and thin and, of course, very toughened by the outdoor life he led as one of Scott Farnham's stock riders. Sue's appearance was so different as to be ludicrous, for she was small and plump with rosy cheeks and a happy smile which appeared immediately she saw Jane alighting from the train. Both came forward to introduce themselves. Hands were heartily shaken, appraisals were made all round, smiles exchanged and within seconds—or so it seemed—Jane was perfectly at her ease. And only then did she realise that behind all the excitement there had been a small but nagging worry that things might not start right. Yes, she was a firm believer that if a thing did not start right then there was little hope of its eventual success.

Little did she realise how wrong that philosophy was!

For now, though, all *had* started right—the train

arriving on time, the couple being there on time, and a very reliable car waiting to take her on the last stage of the long—and often tedious—journey.

'We'll have to camp tonight,' Lanky was saying as he and Sue picked up Jane's biggest suitcases. 'But Margaret will have told you about that?'

'Yes, she did.' Jane was hurrying along with the rest of her luggage, towards the overlanding car where, she noticed, there were water bags fixed to the bumpers. 'We'll be in tents?' She made her voice sound light but she did wonder what she would feel like when darkness dropped on this strange and lonely scene.

'Under canvas, yes.' Lanky was stowing away the luggage in the trunk while Jane put her smaller bags onto the back seat of the car. 'Perhaps you'd like Sue to share your tent?'

'I—er—think I might prefer that,' she was forced to admit and the other two laughed a little.

'There's absolutely nothing to scare you,' Sue assured her but added that she would willingly share Jane's tent if that was what she wanted. Jane thought she would decide later, when darkness was upon them.

They were in the car and speeding along the Bitumen at over ninety miles an hour and Jane just clung to her seat in the back, praying that the 'perfection' mentioned by Margaret, and always insisted on by the Boss, applied to Lanky's driving.

The sun was setting when eventually she heard them talking about making camp for the night. Colours of unbelievable variety lit the sky as the great saffron ball slid beneath the rising sphere of the earth—dazzling gold and glittering bronze mingling with delicate mauves and lilacs and gentle pinks and greens.

Jane gasped inwardly as this phenomenon unfolded before her astonished gaze. She felt the long journey she had just undertaken had been worth while if only for this spectacle, which was already being transformed as the purple shades of twilight changed all the shapes around her, softening the atmosphere, making way for the appearance of millions of stars and the starkly defined outline of a crescent moon.

Lanky drew the car off the Highway and soon it was crunching to a halt on the bank of a dry creek bed where coolibah trees lent some shelter, and it was beneath these that the tents were pitched. Food seemed to come along as if by magic, and a beaker of steaming coffee was placed on the groundsheet beside Jane. She was thrilled with the novelty and when the time came for them to settle down she assured the couple that she would be all right on her own in the smaller of the two tents.

The road became bumpy and this was a sign that the estate was not too far away. It was almost noon on the day following Jane's arrival in Goulalong and Lanky said very good time had been made.

'I knew it was a long way to drive,' said Jane after he seemed to have adopted an apologetic manner. 'Margaret had warned me that I'd be more than a full day and night getting to the homestead.'

'Well, it'll not be too long now.' He indicated the

surrounding lands. 'This is the Bush, made up mainly of scrub and eucalyptus. Soon you'll be seeing the Boss's cattle and some of his stockmen.'

'There,' supplied Sue after another three quarters of an hour had gone by, 'those men are belonging to our outfit.'

Jane looked at the group of men on horseback who seemed to be crowding around something.

'What—?'

'A bore trough,' explained Sue at once. 'They're letting the horses drink. We get water from a vast artesian basin which lies beneath the wilderness of the Inland.'

Jane nodded her head.

'Margaret told me a lot in her last couple of letters.'

'We were sorry when she said she was leaving.'

'She enjoyed being here but she wants to get married.'

'We asked her to try and persuade her boy-friend to come here and settle.' Sue gave a sigh of regret at losing her friend.

'Would Mr. Farnham have found him a job, though?'

'I expect so. He's never turned anyone away yet that we know of. Men come along for a night's kip and often decide they'd like to stay for a while, so the Boss gives them a job. We're always needing rouseabouts.'

'Rouseabouts? Margaret never mentioned them.'

'They do all kinds of jobs around the station—can usually turn their hands to anything. We've three here, two Irish and a Scot.'

'What are their names?'

'Paddy One and Paddy Two. The Scot's name is Ian but we call him Jock.'

'Paddy One and Paddy Two. . . . ' Amusement in Jane's voice but she was thinking: can't get away from the name, Paddy.

'One came a couple of months after the other so someone dubbed them One and Two.' Lanky paused a moment and then, 'By the way, don't go addressing the Boss as Mr. Farnham. We all call him Boss; it's traditional in the Outback. All station owners are called Boss.'

Jane frowned and said nothing. Sue, as if sensing something amiss, turned her head and regarded Jane's expression for a space.

'You don't like the idea?'

'Not really.'

'Well, as Lanky said, it's traditional so you'll have to conform. You'll soon realise that it would sound most odd for you to call him Mr. Farnham when everyone else calls him Boss.'

Jane decided she would avoid addressing him if it were at all possible. She did not suppose, anyway, that he would come into contact with one of his menials working in the kitchen.

'There's the homestead,' Lanky was saying when another few miles had been covered. 'You can't see the front from here but it really is impressive. Did Margaret send you a photo of it?'

'No, but she described the house so well that I feel I'll not meet with many surprises.'

'Georgian and elegant both outside and in. The Boss's grandparents were collectors of antiques; they used to travel all over Europe picking things up. However, I believe the place was cluttered in the end and the Boss's mother sorted it out. Then the Boss himself has done a bit of culling and Sue thinks the result's just great.'

'Everything blends now,' she told Jane.

'Are the—er—Boss's parents dead?'

'Yes. His mother died about eight years ago—we weren't here then. And his father died of a heart attack two years last Easter.'

'Scott had been running the station for a couple of years before then, though,' inserted Lanky. 'His father seemed to lose interest and wanted to sit and read all the time.'

'He was old, though,' supplied Sue. 'Seventy-one when he died.'

'That's the airstrip you can see over there.' Lanky made a sweep of his hand. Jane saw the strip, white and brittle in the sunshine. A small airplane stood at one end, wings painted blue and white. 'The Boss's plane,' elucidated Sue unnecessarily. 'He flies into Winangro at least once a month and if you have shopping to do he'll let you go along with him.'

'If there's room,' supplemented her husband as he turned the great overlanding car into a wide avenue of casuarina trees.

'It's a four-seater,' said Sue, 'and so he can take three others with him. You'll get your turn.'

Jane was not too sure she wanted to go to town with the formidable Boss of Jacana Downs. Already she felt sure they would have nothing in common—he so obviously exalted while she was to be a mere servant in his gracious home. Her thoughts winged to Margaret who seemed to like Scott Farnham despite the fact that she had admitted to his being arrogant and superior. Obviously he had noticed *her*, because he hadn't wanted her to leave his employ. And he had thought so much of her that he had readily agreed to employ the girl whom she had recommended to take her place.

'At last,' breathed Sue getting out of the car as if she had cramp. 'Aren't you tired, Jane?'

'A little. But the excitement's kept me alert,' she added with a little deprecating laugh. Sue looked at her, thinking that she had never seen anyone quite so attractive, and yet so obviously modest regarding her looks. Sue envied her the clear alabaster skin that revealed so intriguingly the blue veins at her temples. The cheek bones were high and delicately formed, the nose upturned just enough to add to the attractions of rosy lips and high wide brow. The eyes were sapphire blue, large and faintly slanting upwards at the outer corners; the hair—perfect foil for the facial beauty— was of deep gold laced with bronze and tawny brown. Long, to her shoulders, it flicked up at the ends and the little quiff at the left temple would always be unruly, thought Sue—and envied Jane that, too. Men would find her interesting—not that there were many men to spare on Jacana Downs, not the kind who would suit Jane, that was. The Boss himself was spoken for but even if he'd been free he'd not have shown the least interest in this girl, lovely as she was.

No, the Boss was far too aware of his own superiority to demean himself by noticing one of his employees. Sue's thoughts drifted momentarily to Daphne and she frowned. Life at Jacana Downs would not be quite the same when she became mistress and Sue was glad that Daphne and Lanky had the bungalow. Like all the others it was some distance from the homestead, one of many which formed what could almost be called a small village since there was a general store, a school and a hospital in addition to the dispensary where one could buy some of the items found in any chemist's shop. Here one could also get a hair-cut and a shampoo and set if necessary. Anita ran this establishment and her sister did the hairdressing.

A lubra appeared at the door and Lanky spoke to her. Jane was looking up at the imposing Georgian façade with its fine pillars around which trailing plants had found support. The door was high and wide and solid, like the house, thought Jane. She felt happy to be living in such a stately home and a smile was fluttering on her lips as the horse and rider swept into her view.

'The Boss,' said Lanky and the next moment he was there, swinging from the horse and a rouseabout had appeared unobtrusively to take the bridle and lead the animal away. Jane stared up into the sun-bitten face of the man for whom she was going to work. Not many surprises, she had said! Well, prepared as she was for this man's attractiveness she had never visualised anyone quite as superlative as he. Six feet two or three, he towered above her, lithe and muscled with broad shoulders and slender waist and hips. He wore a checked shirt tucked into tight-fitting riding breeches, high boots and a slouch hat which he was tilting to the back of his head. His features, firmly etched, spelled strength of character, his deep-set grey eyes forcefulness and authority. Like some overlord, he seemed to Jane, staring down from his superior height in such a way as to make her feel even smaller than she was. This sensation of inferiority was most unpleasant to say the least, and it was entirely new to Jane who at twenty-three had acquired a fair share of confidence owing to her position of private secretary to the Managing Director of the firm for which she had worked until a week ago. She almost tilted her chin and thought better of it. She did not want to be sacked even before she had started!

'You had a good journey?' The voice carried the Australian drawl which was so evident in Lanky's tone but with Scott it seemed almost clipped. Certainly it was cool.

'Yes, thank you,' returned Jane. 'The car part was long but interesting.'

Scott held out his hand.

'Welcome to Jacana Downs,' he said as she slipped her hand into his and then winced as her fingers were crushed. 'I hope you'll be as happy with us as your friend Margaret was.'

'I hope so too.' She felt shy, inadequate, but there was something else, too, some other unfathomable emotion that disturbed her faintly.

'Sue,' he said, 'do you know where Jane is to sleep?'

'Yes, Anna told me it was to be the corner room facing west.'

'Take her up, then, and afterwards you can show her around. You don't mind? You're not too tired?'

'Not for a pleasant task like this,' smiled Sue. 'Shall I have time before tea to introduce her to one or two of the wives?'

'I should think so.' He glanced at his watch and nodded. 'Perhaps you and Lanky would like to have tea with us?'

'Thanks, Boss,' from Lanky. 'I'll see to the car and then get changed.'

The room to which she was shown made Jane stare in disbelief.

'It's for me—a room like this?' No servant's room, she thought as she glanced around, noting the soft lilac wall to wall carpeting, the paler walls and white ceiling with its ornate coving. The furniture was of Regency design, the bed large and draped with an embroidered cover of the same lilac shade as the curtains which framed the high wide window. The bathroom was *en suite*, in pampas green with gold-plated fittings and hanging plants reflected in the mirrors which occupied two of the walls. Luxury everywhere even to the high quality of the towels which were folded neatly on a glass shelf. 'I can hardly believe it!' she exclaimed. 'Are you sure you haven't made a mistake. . . .' But even as she spoke her voice trailed, for there was her luggage, visible through the open door of what was obviously a small dressing-room.

'The Boss likes to make his staff as comfortable as possible. Margaret had a room similar to this one but that's been made ready for the Boss's cousin and her daughter who are coming for a visit—' Sue stopped to ponder a moment. 'I think it's this coming weekend that they're expected. They're nice so you'll enjoy their company.'

'Are they young—I mean, the daughter must be a child?'

'No. Crystal's about your age—twenty-one or two, I should think. Her mother's in her early forties.'

'Widowed?'

'Divorced.'

'They come often?'

'A couple of times a year.' A small pause ensued. 'Didn't Margaret ever mention them?'

'No; she probably didn't think it important. We didn't correspond all that regularly. It was only when she was coming home that she wrote to suggest I apply for the job.'

Sue looked her over speculatively.

'Think you'll like being a skivvy?' she asked in some amusement. 'You were a private secretary, you said.'

'The change will do me good. It's experience, and lots of girls—and men—travel in this way, taking all kinds of jobs in order to gain experience of other countries and cultures. I feel sure I'm going to take to the life here.'

'It's lonely. Have you thought of that?'

Jane nodded at once, saying that Margaret had mentioned the loneliness. 'But she knows I'm fairly capable of finding my own entertainment,' added Jane with a smile. 'One can't ever be lonely if there's a book available.'

'The Boss has a very interesting library.' Sue paused as Jane slipped off the fine woollen jacket she wore over her blouse and skirt. 'Ready to look around or do you want to freshen up first?'

Jane cast a glance into the full-length mirror and grimaced.

'I'll have a wash and change my clothes. What time is tea?'

'Four o'clock. We have it on the verandah—at least, the Boss does. I'm not usually here.'

'Do you work in the house?'

'Two days a week but I finish at half-past three and go off to get our evening meal under way.' She moved towards the door. 'I'll leave you for a quarter of an hour or so. If you want Anna or Gelda to unpack for you just ring the bell. It's over there, in the corner.'

'They're the lubras?'

'That's right. They do all the hardest chores like washing and cleaning. You'll do the lighter work— bedrooms and perhaps some polishing. Mainly your job's cooking. Your friend found that hard work.'

Margaret had put her in the picture regarding her duties and cooking seemed to be the most important, with the unmarried stockmen coming in early in the morning for huge breakfasts of steaks and eggs and lashings of toast. Then there were the refreshments which the men would carry with them and eat when they stopped for smoke-oh. Jane had asked Sue what smoke-oh was.

24

'It's just the break the men have for elevenses,' was Sue's casual rejoinder.

Some of the men ate in the kitchen at the homestead of an evening but in the main they went to their quarters and cooked something up for themselves. Many of the stockmen were in any case miles away from the homestead and Jane was later to learn that there were several other 'villages' scattered about the estate—and about every estate of this magnitude. She wondered just how many employees Scott Farnham had. Some were Aborigines, Sue had told her, proud men who once had been quite capable of 'going walkabout'—back to the wild—but they were so well treated by Scott that they very rarely went off. If they did, though, they would always be taken back on their return, for Scott was a most understanding man who realised that this wish for freedom to roam the wild rangelands was inherent and could not be stamped out until many more generations had come and gone.

Jane worked swiftly when Sue had left. She partly unpacked one suitcase to find a cotton dress and some underwear. She had a shower, dried herself quickly and by the time Sue returned twenty minutes later she was feeling fresh and clean and ready to be introduced to some of the stockmen's wives.

But first of all she was shown the main rooms on the ground floor of the house—the sitting-room elegantly furnished with antiques, all of the Georgian period; the dining-room which had a magnificent Waterford chandelier above the long polished table. The Regency chairs were upholstered with the same material as the long drapes framing the two broad windows. The carpet of dove grey was thick and soft beneath Jane's feet and she wondered just how much the fitting out of this house had cost.

'Mr. Farnham must be a millionaire,' she murmured almost to herself.

'A few times over,' added Sue with a grimace. 'No one should be as rich as these graziers—although I do have to admit that the Boss never flaunts what he has. He's very modest as regards his personal requirements.'

'It seems that these graziers are always working,' commented Jane as she and Sue entered the library.

'They live for the wild outdoors, for horses and cattle and the smooth running of their estates.' Sue paused to let Jane take in the great variety of books lining the shelves. 'It'll be an altogether new life for you. I hope you'll stay with us for a while.'

'I shall,' answered Jane with conviction. 'I know I'm going to like it here.'

Outside, they strolled through the grounds, ablaze with flowers and with the lawns being well-watered by several sprinklers trained upon them. A flock of pink galahs flew by and settled in some eucalypts which lined the dry bed of the creek which meandered through the grounds of the house. In a tall bush a kookaburra began to laugh and Jane automatically stopped to listen.

'He really does laugh!' she exclaimed.

'Of course, and it's infectious! If you stay here another minute you'll be laughing your head off yourself.'

Jane's eyes were already filled with laughter. She

was thrilled with the novelty of everything she was seeing and experiencing.

She wished she had come out before . . . before she had met the fiancé of one of her best friends. . . .

Paddy's image came to her mind again as she walked along by Sue's side towards the road leading to the colony of bungalows.

Jane had avoided a goodbye scene with Paddy, although she had called on Mary the night before she was leaving. She had rung first so knew Paddy would not be there. 'Paddy will be so disappointed at not seeing you,' Mary had said. 'Say goodbye to him for me,' was Jane's only response to that and she had abruptly changed the subject. She now fervently hoped that he and Mary would be happy together and that the wedding would go through without a hitch. For herself—she had collected a scar but only a small one—for she had retreated before any further attack could be made on her heart. She now had new surroundings and no problems; she would forget Paddy in a very short space of time.

The first bungalow at which they stopped was prettily embellished with climbing plants round the door and along the windowsills; the lawn was smooth and green; the paintwork on the house newly done. Neatness and pride in possession characterised most of the bungalows, Jane was soon to discover.

Alison Dale was the wife of Reuben the head stockman. Small and dainty but well on the wrong side of forty, she was greying a little and her face was lined; the result of the sun, Jane surmised, rather than the result of age. She was eager to meet the newcomer and would have had them take refreshments but Sue explained about the tea they were soon to have.

'We've all been looking forward to seeing Margaret's friend,' Alison was saying as they prepared to leave. 'Margaret was so popular here that we began to wish the Boss would fall for her and she'd be staying forever.' Laughter edged the soft voice as she added, 'Alas for our hopes! Margaret had someone else and the Boss had set his heart on Daphne Woolcott.' A small pause and then, 'Have you a boy-friend back home?'

Jane shook her head.

'No, I haven't, so I can stay here as long as I like.'

'We'll have a little get-together one afternoon and you can meet all the others.'

'Yes—' Sue was glancing at her watch. 'I don't think we have time for any more visits, Jane. The Boss could just do his nut if we're late.'

'Not on Jane's first day,' argued Alison. 'Even he isn't as bad as that.'

'Even he. . . .' Sounded ominous, decided Jane and hoped that the one fly in the ointment didn't turn out to be the arrogant owner of Jacana Downs.

Chapter Two

It was with something akin to relief that Jane heard Anna say,

'Mrs. Feldwick and her daughter will be arriving this evening. The Boss is taking the plane to meet them off the train.'

'Where are they coming from?' Jane later inquired of Sue. She had decided to have her hair shampooed and set and to her delight she met Sue in the shop, also intending to have her hair done.

'Sydney. They have an apartment there.'

'Don't they work?'

'Oh, yes. They have a small gown shop—rather exclusive. They're lucky in that they have a most reliable assistant who looks after the place whenever they're away.'

'I'm glad they're coming,' mused Jane, her eyes on the woman under the drier. She was the schoolteacher but this was Saturday so there was no school. She saw Jane and smiled. They were a great crowd, Jane had decided on being introduced to some more of the wives. As yet she had not met many of the men—just those who came in for breakfast and the rouseabouts who lived in at the homestead, Paddy One and Two and the Scotsman, Jock, youngish and obviously taken with Jane.

'Why—fed up with your own company?' Sue appeared slightly anxious until Jane shook her head.

'No, it isn't that. I've been kept busy in any case. It's—well—a strain, rather, having dinner every night with the Boss. I hadn't expected to be eating with him regularly.'

'I must say I was rather surprised myself when you mentioned the arrangement. Perhaps he's troubled that you'd feel out of place eating in the kitchen with the lubras.'

'Margaret did.'

'Yes, but for most of the time she was here there was another home help, Stella from the south of England. Wonder Margaret didn't mention her.'

'Margaret didn't write much at first—I think I told you that?'

'Yes. Well, this Stella and Margaret palled up and so they wouldn't mind eating together in the kitchen. As you have no one the Boss must have decided to be polite and let you dine with him.'

'It's a strain,' said Jane again, relieved to see Avril being taken from under the drier. Jane never did have much patience when waiting in the hair-dresser's.

'Then why don't you eat in the kitchen?'

'I don't like to suggest it.' She wouldn't really like to eat in the kitchen; she had never been used to it at home where her mother, following the genteel pattern of her own childhood and youth in a small stately manor, had always insisted that as meals were social events they should be eaten in a pretty setting, hence the regular use of her dining-room.

'Well, you'll be having company for a while now,' said Sue. 'I'm sure you'll get along splendidly with the two who are coming this evening.'

It was several hours later when, having missed the arrival of the two women because she was in the kitchen doing all the preliminaries for the evening meal, which would be served by the lubras, Jane met Crystal and her mother.

Scott made the introduction as soon as Jane, in a flowered evening dress, arrived on the verandah for pre-dinner drinks. As usual he was superbly dressed in the appropriate clothes, this time wearing a white tropical suit which contrasted most attractively with the burnt-ochre of his skin.

'How do you do?' Mrs. Feldwick said graciously as she looked Jane over swiftly. 'Are you settling in all right?'

'Very well, thank you,' smiled Jane, aware that the Boss was for some reason appearing to be more interested in her than usual. She felt his intense gaze on her as she turned to Crystal and extended a hand.

'What can I get you, Jane?'

'Sherry, please.' Jane took the chair he indicated with a negligent flick of his hand. 'Did you have a pleasant journey?' she inquired for something to say.

'Not very. I dislike travelling but love it when I get here. Scott's so hospitable, the perfect host, and so we come as often as we can.' Mrs. Feldwick was smiling affectionately at his broad back. A small silence fell then and Jane's eyes wandered to the girl. Yes, she was about her own age, dark with a rounded, pretty face and eyes that were something between grey and green, wide and frank with a fringe of curling dark lashes.

Her mother was equally attractive but in an entirely different way. Serene and cool, with a clear complexion and dark hair immaculately coiffured to include a French pleat to the left side, she at first appeared to be rather aloof, superior like her cousin. But the smile, slow but sincere, detracted from the impression of austerity and made her human, attractive in a compelling way which, decided Jane, ran in the family because of late she had reluctantly admitted that the Boss was compellingly attractive too, drawing her at times in a way that was disturbing to say the least.

Jane didn't want him to appeal to her in *that* way; she'd had enough with Paddy and wanted only to remain heart-free for a very long time to come.

Scott was showing another side of his personality from that to which Jane had become used in the five days she had been at Jacana Downs. Hitherto he had been politely cool, showing the minimum of interest in Jane so that conversation had always flagged, hence the reason for her telling Sue that dining with him was a strain. This evening, though, he was the gracious, interested host, with ears for everything that was said by any one of the three women. Mrs. Feldwick was keen to know how Jane was taking to the life; she asked numerous questions without hesitation or apology. Jane answered, profoundly aware that Scott was just as interested as his cousin.

'So you had no real reason for coming?' Mrs. Feldwick said. 'You just wanted a change, a bit of adventure?'

'That's right.' The lie came glibly but Jane knew she had coloured slightly, knew too that Scott's keen eyes had noticed and she wondered if he were curious as to the reason for it. She hated the idea that he might conclude she had told a lie.

'And how long are you intending to stay?' It was Crystal who put the question and Jane turned in her direction.

'I can't say. I'm very happy here and like the change.'

'And the work?' Scott's deep-set grey eyes became keenly questioning as they looked directly into hers. 'It's not what you've been used to.'

'No, but I'm adaptable.'

'It's menial in comparison.' Scott lifted his glass from the rattan table at his elbow and sipped the aperitif slowly, his eyes still on Jane's face which registered surprise at the remark.

'Menial, yes, but honest work could never disgrace anyone.'

'A splendid philosophy,' applauded Mrs. Feldwick. 'One could sweep the streets or deal with garbage and still retain one's dignity.'

'Of course,' returned Jane matter-of-factly. 'If I were desperate I'd do anything rather than be out of work.' She looked again at Scott, to find his eyes still focused on her.

'I admire your doctrine, Jane.' Scott's firm mouth curved in a smile which seemed to send a pleasant but unwanted tingle along Jane's spine. Why was the man so darned attractive! She knew a sudden resentment against him and anger against herself for the way she was allowing him to affect her. Just because he had unbent a little, had smiled at her, said something flattering to her by saying he admired her doctrine.

She thought of Paddy and wondered if she were one of those stupid females who were susceptible to any man who was physically attractive. But no. It had never happened until the advent of Paddy. And now. . . . Well, perhaps it was excusable to be attracted by a man of Scott Farnham's masculine perfection. He had just about everything to make a woman's imagination run riot—a superb physique and the litheness of an athlete, handsome features with the added characteristics acquired by the outdoor life he led, a certain charm of manner and pose that had nothing to do with the majestic way he walked or gestured—or even spoke, with that finely timbred voice enhanced by the slow and quiet Australian drawl.

Conversation drifted into less personal channels for a while and then Mrs. Feldwick said,

'How's the romance getting along, Scott? Last time we were here I had a feeling you'd be engaged when we made our next appearance.'

He shrugged and said,

'Not yet, Rachel. There's plenty of time.' Leaning forward, he placed his glass on the table again. Jane looked at the hand, the long brown fingers betraying strength in spite of their slenderness.

'You're not a youngster,' his cousin reminded him and he grimaced. 'And Daphne's no chicken either. How old is she—twenty-eight?'

'I believe she's twenty-seven,' with the lifting of a hand to hide a yawn.

'Believe?' repeated Rachel with a quirk of an eyebrow. 'Don't you know the age of your lady love?'

He laughed and fixed her gaze.

'Stop match-making, Rachel. I shall enter the inevitable net when I become tired of my own company.'

'Fighting shy, eh? The confirmed bachelor, or perhaps you would like people to regard you as immune? You can't leave Jacana without an heir, Scott.'

Again he lifted a lean brown hand to mask a yawn. Jane knew it was for effect and her eyes were twinkling as they met his.

'I'm not particularly interested in what happens when I'm dead,' he commented. 'Can I get you another drink, Crystal?'

'Snubbed, am I?' laughed his cousin. 'I can take it, though. I always have, from you.' She fell silent, watching him refill her daughter's glass. 'Most men want an heir,' she said.

'Perhaps Scott wants to marry for love.' It was plain that Crystal had spoken without thinking. Jane watched with renewed interest to see how Scott took this. But it was his cousin who broke the silence.

'What on earth makes you think that he doesn't love Daphne!'

'I . . .' Crystal went red. 'I didn't think what I was saying.' Confused, she averted her head and stared down into her glass.

'Shall we change the subject?' from Scott in suave decisive tones. 'Jane, we were talking about your work here and I was saying it was different from what you had been used to. You were a private secretary, your friend Margaret told me.'

Jane nodded her head.

'That's right.'

'You were happy in that kind of work?'

'Yes, of course I was.' She naturally refrained from mentioning her unpredictable boss whose attitude towards her had often brought forth the comment from some colleague or another:

'How the devil do you put up with his tantrums, Jane?'

The salary was good; she more often than not knew how to deal with Joseph Bligh's 'tantrums' and so life at work wasn't nearly so bad as most people believed. Nevertheless, she had come away with a sense of relief rather than regret, since a change was certainly overdue.

'Yet you can accept the work in the kitchen—and say you are happy with it?'

She frowned slightly. What exactly was he getting at?

'I'm happy with the change,' she said, conscious of two other pairs of eyes fixed upon her.

Scott said nothing more on the subject and during dinner his conversation was mainly with his visitors. Jane was brought in of course but she felt it was merely out of politeness and good manners and as soon as the meal was finished she asked to be excused.

'You're not going to bed?' frowned Rachel with a hint of concern in her quiet voice.

'I—well, I do feel rather tired,' she said.

'We're having coffee and liqueurs on the verandah,' said Scott. 'I'm sure you'd like to join us.' He was all charm again . . . and again she was conscious of emotions that were new and although not too troublesome she did feel a faintly disturbing vibration of nerves, unfamiliar and resented.

They went out together and were served by Anna, big and buxom and stolid as the Sphynx in her expression. Dark-skinned and with premature lines round eyes and mouth, she had about her that certain air of dignity which characterised all those who were native to the ancient soil of the Inland and the desert.

Jane leant back in her upholstered chair and tried not to look at her employer. But his firm profile silhouetted against the night's purple darkness drew her attention and fixed it so that she could not drag her eyes away. The two women were talking quietly while sipping their coffee; Scott turned his head as if aware suddenly of the fixed interest of his home help. She averted her head swiftly and hoped the dimness of the amber lights above her head effectively hid the tinge of embarrassment that had stained her cheeks. To be caught staring at him like that! What must he think of her? She found herself wondering if he were already beginning to assume she had a crush on him— She halted her thoughts but they thrust themselves into her consciousness instantly. Crush. . . .

Was this sensation of being drawn to him a crush? She had never met any man with this kind of compelling personality and distinctive magnetism and she found herself admitting that he was a man it was impossible to ignore. His very presence affected the atmosphere; he seemed to be a vital part of it.

She thought of Daphne, whom she had not yet met, and something weighty and unpleasant pressed against the nerves of her stomach.

'You're very quiet, Jane.' His voice severed her musings and slowly she lifted her head. She looked beyond him and upwards, to where the heavens were brightest, the Southern Cross spangling them, a tapestry of silver in bouyant suspension against the purple velvet of an Australian sky.

'I'm just relaxing, and enjoying the peace,' she said, a smile hovering on her lips. She felt strangely at peace in spite of the weight that still pressed upon her. 'It's wonderful here, in the cool of the night and the feeling of isolation from the rest of mankind.' She paused to note his expression and found it unfathomable. 'Do you feel the detachment too—or are you so used to it you don't notice?' It was the first time she had spoken with such freedom and ease; she felt herself to be his equal, although she had no illusions that he was feeling the same way about her.

'I notice,' he answered in his slow and quiet drawl. 'So you like the isolation?'

'Yes. It's so restful . . . like returning to the primitive before man appeared to sully the earth.' She had been talking almost to herself and she coloured up again on hearing Rachel exclaim,

'My, but we're getting on to a deep subject! *Primitive*, Jane? Do you mean to say you'd like to go back in time and live before the age of progress?'

Jane laughed rather shakily and said she'd like to go back even farther than that, much farther.

'But in that case, my dear, you'd not be here now. Surely life is precious to you?'

'Oh, yes, of course. I was merely dreaming, allowing my imagination to run riot. One can never ever go back—not with any success.' She spoke in a lowered tone, again almost to herself for she was thinking of Paddy and feeling glad she'd had the strength of character to come away before any real harm was done. She would never go back while there was the least danger of her losing her heart to Paddy, or of him losing his to her.

'Not with any success,' repeated Scott; there was something of a question in the words and he was subjecting her to a curious scrutiny. 'It sounds as if there were a hidden quality in what you said?'

She coloured delicately.

'No—why should there be?'

He shrugged as if with sudden impatience and his tone was coolly dispassionate when next he spoke.

'I guess you had a very good reason for coming out here, but of course it's your own business.'

She felt snubbed and as soon as it was possible she again asked to be excused. This time there was no attempt to stop her from leaving but once in her room she felt inexplicably restless and, convinced she would not be able to sleep yet awhile, she decided to take a stroll outside. She kept to the back of the house in order to remain out of sight of those on the verandah, not knowing that the two women had said good night to Scott almost immediately after she had left the verandah.

She saw the shadowy figure crossing her path and halted. But Scott had sensed her presence and she bit her lip with vexation as he turned his head then stopped, obviously waiting for her to come up to him. She hesitated, then realised she was surely looking foolish, standing here, for no reason at all. She said awkwardly as she reached him,

'I felt I wouldn't sleep so I decided to take a walk. It's—it's very pleasant out here.' Did he know just how embarrassed she was? Jane rather thought he would know because she had already sensed his uncanny perception.

'I find it so,' he agreed without expression. 'Which way were you going?' They were at a sort of cross-roads, with a wide lawn spreading away to their left. The gleam of the swimming pool was to their right but some distance away; it looked silver-blue in the moonlight, its surface shimmering as a result of the mechanical circulation of the water. It was a pretty sight, with its backcloth of tall palms, like sentinels against the star-spangled, Capricornian sky. Other trees swayed gently, foliage bright and argent-tinted. Oleanders formed a protective hedge around two sides of the pool and along another side were changing huts and a flower-draped patio where white chairs and a table stood out against the darker background of hibiscus bushes.

'I wasn't intending to ·take any specific path,' she answered at length. 'I just want to wander.'

'You've done this before?'

She nodded at once, automatically falling into step beside him as he moved and then belatedly wondering if he would rather be alone.

'Yes, once or twice.'

'Don't go out of the grounds at night.'

'No? Not even if I keep the homestead in sight?'

'Has anyone mentioned scrub bulls to you?'

'No—what are they?' She matched her steps to his and an access of excitement tingled her nerve-ends. Vaguely she was recalling that she never felt quite like this about Paddy.

'Bulls gone wild. They're about sometimes and you never know just when or where you'll come face to face with one. They're dangerous so be warned.'

She shivered at the idea of being faced with a massive wild bull out there in the bush.

'I can't go out in the daytime, then—not outside the grounds?'

'Yes, you can walk but keep yourself alert. You'd like to ride, no doubt? Margaret spent a good deal of her free time either riding or swimming.'

'I can have a horse?' Her voice was eager, her big eyes limpid and happy as she raised them to his. 'Thank you very much, Mr.—er. . . .' She had never yet felt comfortable at calling him Boss to his men even though she knew she would have to get used to it sometime.

He sent his glance from her face to her figure as if to put her at her ease. But he said without much expression,

'I believe you know how to address me?'

She coloured in the moonlight.

'Yes, I've been told.'

'But you don't like it?'

She bit her lip.

'I'm sorry. It's just that—that it makes me feel inferior—and—and embarrassed.'

He slanted her a glance, one eyebrow raised.

'Nevertheless, you will have to get used to it.' Crisp the tone and firm. 'You'd feel far more embarrassed should anyone hear you address me as Mr. Farnham.'

'Yes—Sue told me.' She changed the subject abruptly. 'I think I'll turn in now.' They had passed the pool, skirting the patio and were now in a less formal part of the grounds. There was a perfume in the air and she paused to look around.

'The frangipani over there,' indicated Scott with a raised finger. 'Its other name is the Temple Tree. You like the perfume?'

'It's delightful! What are the flowers like?' She could not see them, of course, although she could see the tree itself.

'Creamy white and delicate.' His voice was low, appreciative. Jane darted him an upward glance, amazed at the idea that this toughened giant of the great outdoors could be sentimental about a flower.

'I must come along in the morning and have a look.' They were still walking, away from the lights of the gardens, into the dimness of the more wooded region of the homestead grounds. Jane found she was tingling with an inexplicable sense of expectation. For the air around her seemed vibrant, the atmosphere between her and Scott tense . . . as if they were on the edge of a precipice.

Bewildered and unsure of herself, she repeated her intention of going inside.

'Very well, Jane. I'll walk with you.'

'It doesn't matter,' she began but he interrupted her.

'It's dark and lonely here. I'd better come with you.'

She started in surprise, wondering greatly at this change in his attitude towards her, for until this evening he had seemed hardly to notice her at all. He stopped; she stared up in the darkness, sensing his interest, and then his frown. He was close, so close that she was vitally conscious of the pervasive smell of after-shave mingling with the sense-stirring male odour of him.

Jane swallowed, affected as she had never been

affected before and suddenly she knew she must get away, quickly. And in her haste she swung around without realising that the ground was made bumpy by aerial roots which, as she stepped on one, sent her staggering off-balance. Strong hands caught her before she fell; she was brought with a jerk against the whipcord hardness of Scott's body and before she could even try to get her breath back her mouth was covered with his. The kiss was fierce and sensuous, his lips moistly exploring, compelling her to part hers. Quivers of erotic desire were shot through every nerve cell as this awakening experience swam freely through her half-protesting frame. She seemed to be robbed of the strength to object when his hand, warm and sensuous, closed on the virginal lobe of one high firm breast. An ache of swift longing affected her loins, forcing her to strain against him, succumbing to the mastery of his own insistent rhythm. The world around her spun with her loss of control; she slid her arms about his neck, thrilling to the awareness that her caress on his nape was as exciting to him as it was to her. His sinewed frame was possessed of a strength that left her gasping and with the sure knowledge that she was collecting bruises. His hardness was pain as well as pleasure; his exploring hands as they now slid with arrogant possession along her thighs were as savagely hurtful as they were amorously gentle.

'You're . . . desirable, Jane.' His mouth was hot against her cheek, his hands searching and insistent as they slid even farther down her body. An infusion of desire sent spasms through her and she thrilled to his reciprocation, to the knowledge that she had stimulated him to the point of diminishing control. She had flashes of thought which made her squirm but sanity was not for moments like this! Intoxicated by the night and the moon and the sense of isolation, she allowed the fever-heat of Scott's love-making to ignite a flame within her which could only be quenched by total and sublime fulfillment.

Abandoned, insensible to what was right and wrong, drawn into the fiery tempest of Scott's almost primitive domination, Jane could not control the words that quivered breathlessly on her lips.

'Love me, Scott. . . .'

'I intend to.' His answer was a gruff and throaty bass tone against the delicate curve of her throat. 'Yes, I intend to. . . .' One lean hand came up; the strap of her dress was brought down from her shoulder . . . and she quivered from head to foot as flesh met flesh in the most intimate situation she had ever been with a man. She felt heady with submission, desiring only to be conquered, brought low by the mastery of Scott's hands and his body. He lifted her and she let her head fall onto his shoulder as he carried her back the way they had come, making for one of the changing rooms by the pool.

After kicking open the door he entered and laid her down on a garden lounger which, she later learned, was one of several brought in there when not in use outside. In the darkness she lay on her back, aware that he was beginning to undress.

'You're more of a sport than I had expected,' she heard him say and it did seem that contempt edged his voice. 'Margaret was far more straight-laced, but then she had ties back home. I presume you have none?'

Jane felt an icy finger running along her spine. Ignoring his question she said in low and tremulous tones,

'Margaret—you tried to—to make love to her?'

'No, but one of the stockmen did. He received a slap across the face and a kick on the shin.'

'And—and so she was respected after that?'

'Very much so.' Scott threw his white jacket onto a chair. 'Yes, your friend was very well liked here— What—!'

Jane had risen, brushed against him in the dark, and was at the door, fumbling for the handle, her breath catching in her throat.

'I want to—to go—!' But Scott's grip was a vice on her wrist, his voice almost harsh above her.

'No you don't! Run out on me, would you?' A low laugh escaped him as, roughly, he seized her chin and forced her head right back. With his elbow he snapped on the light. Jane's heart failed her as she noted his expression. He had no intention of allowing her to change her mind. 'What's the idea, Jane?' he demanded, his tone as rough as his touch. 'Why the change? You were more than willing a moment ago—'

'I was crazy! Out of my mind!' she flared, twisting about in her attempt to be free of his bruising hold on her wrist. 'It was madness, and now I've seen my folly. You spoke of Margaret and—'

'So that was it,' he broke in sardonically. 'I upset you by the comparison. You resented it, didn't you?

Yes, Margaret was very different from you but you must have known it so why the embarrassed maiden stunt? Do you suppose it impresses me after the intimacy of the last quarter of an hour?' Again he laughed, releasing her but standing between her and the door. She drew a trembling hand through her hair, aware of acute perspiration on her forehead and in the palms of her hands. Why, oh why, had she been tempted! It was no wonder that this man despised her, compared her most unfavourably with her friend.

But what if Margaret had been tempted by Scott rather than the stockman? Would she have been so strong then?

Useless questions which could not be answered and Jane chided herself for mentally asking them.

'Please let me go,' she begged, aware of tears glistening on her lashes. 'I was a fool and bitterly regret my weakness. I know you must believe me to be cheap, but I'm not. I've never let a man do—do the -th-things you did. . . .' Hot with embarrassment and humiliation she lowered her head, felt the tears escape and brought up a fist to knuckle her eyes. Whether it was this childish gesture or not she would never know, but without warning his manner changed, miraculously, and he was tilting her chin again but this time rather gently. He looked into her tear-dimmed eyes for a long moment, a tense and electric moment, and she thought he was fighting the impulse to kiss her again. He let her go, and moved from his position of guarding the door. He picked up his coat and put it on.

'Come on,' he commanded abruptly. 'We'll get back to the homestead.' He paused a moment. 'Dry your eyes—' He flipped a handkerchief from his pocket and dangled it before her. 'Use this. You can't go back looking like that—'

'Thank you,' she faltered and began to use the handkerchief.

'The others did say good night as if they were going to bed but you never know. They could have changed their minds and be around when we get back. So make sure you're looking all right.' Slow the voice now, typified by the drawl, but the tone was firm for all that and Jane accepted the small black comb he offered her.

'I'm very sorry,' she quavered as she handed back the comb and handkerchief.

'About *that*? No more sorry than I,' he added with a snort of grim amusement. 'If you aren't willing to go through with it, my girl, then cut out the preliminaries! If you don't you're going to find yourself in trouble one of these days. I warn you, not many of my stockmen have the same sense of chivalry as I.'

He meant to embarrass her and he succeeded. Jane felt the burning intensity of this embarrassment in her cheeks and she put her hands to them unconsciously.

'You obviously think the worst of me,' she said, not having meant to say anything like that at all but it slipped out, a reflection of her unhappy thoughts.

'What else?' he responded dryly. 'I could have taken you out there—' He stopped and spread his hands. 'You're a bit of a puzzle, though,' he admitted with a swift and heavy frown. 'If you're easy then why the sudden change of mind?'

She shook her head, vaguely conscious of the idea that she must leave Jacana Downs just as soon as she could.

'You wouldn't understand,' was all she had to say and as he made no response they walked in silence back to the house.

'Good night,' she said huskily when they reached the verandah and she turned to enter the sitting-room.

'Good night, Jane.' Amusement edged his voice and his mouth quirked at one corner. 'Sleep well.'

She looked at him, ashamed and depressed, yet angry with him because of the part he had played in the drama. Men! They knew their power to tempt, were familiar at an early age with all the tricks—the use of hands and speech and even breath! Jane said with a touch of dignity,

'You will not be surprised when I say I am leaving. How soon can that be arranged? I don't suppose you'll demand a month's notice from me?'

Although he appeared untouched by this, and a hand was lifted to conceal a yawn, there was a certain degree of vexation in his voice when he said,

'Don't be absurd. You can't leave your job for a small thing like that. Go to bed; you'll see it all differently in the morning.' He frowned at her. 'Run along, I said. Self-pity bores me.'

Her eyes blazed at the way he was treating her, like

a petulent child whom he would dearly have loved to spank!

'I shall leave no matter what you say!' she flung at him and turned without another word, tears of anger blinding her vision as she made her way towards the curving, balustraded staircase which lead to the landing off of which her room was situated.

Chapter Three

A pair of kookaburras laughing their heads off outside
her window was the first thing Jane heard on waking
up the following morning. But the consciousness of
them died as memory flooded in and heat brought
swift colour to her cheeks. If only she could disap-
pear! What on earth had come over her last night, out
there in the primitive isolation of the Australian
Outback? Scott, with his determined finesse and his
obvious desires, his ardour let loose on the only
female available at the time. Fury, wild and strong,
obliterated all embarrassment, fury against the man
who had seemed the very last to make advances like
that to a mere servant. He was so aloof and superior,

so arrogant and conscious of his own exalted position as one of the nobility of the Outback, that it now seemed impossible that the scene had taken place at all.

She slid from between the smooth white sheets and stared at herself through the dressing-table mirror, her eyes pensive, her pulse affected by the memories running unwanted through her mind. If only she could forget, wipe out the entire memory! What were Scott's thoughts at this moment? Was he too remembering? Perhaps he was amused, congratulating himself on his victory, which could have been complete had he not mentioned her friend and so brought her violently to her senses.

A sigh of regret was the prelude to tears gathering behind her eyes and she brushed them angrily. Why should she be crying when the man to blame was probably laughing? If and when she met him during the day she would adopt an attitude of aloof indifference, just as if the occurrence was nothing more than a mere incident which she had almost forgotten.

She took a warm scented bath, dressed in denims and a striped shirt, and made her way down to the massive kitchen where the two lubras were already there to help with the cooking. Men began drifting in, big men and tough, some with beards almost smothering their faces; others clean-shaven with skins gleaming like the patina of old, well-used leather. All wore belted denims and strong leather boots, some caked with an accumulation of dust, others shining as if their owners were proud to be wearing them. Checked shirts seemed to be the fashion for most of the men, and when out on the range all wore slouch hats, usually turned down at the sides and up at the front. Sensible attire for the job they had to do.

'More steak, Anna,' from Matt who was English and ruggedly handsome except for the scar running vividly along his left cheek. He had been thrown by a scrub bull and rescued by Scott at the risk of Scott's own safety.

'I'll get it.' Jane wiped greasy hands down her apron and picked up a large fork. The chunk of meat was consumed within seconds of her putting it on Matt's plate. He was sprawling at one end of the scrubbed teak table; she noticed his hands, knuckles enlarged and bright as bronze. Along one side of the same table others sat eating mountains of steak and lamb chops while one or two had ham and eggs. The lubras were busy making a mountain of toast. Jane stood over the stove, sweat standing out in little beads on her forehead. She turned, nerves tingling, fork in hand, and looked up into the calm and arrogant face of her employer. For one intense moment they stared at one another, she hot and much the worse for her hour and a half over the stove, he cool and incredibly immaculate despite his clothes. But the denims were newly laundered—he put on clean ones every day, sometimes twice a day—his shirt of plain blue cotton starched and fresh. His boots shone, his hands, though toughened like those of his stockmen, were spotlessly clean, the nails well-cared for.

'Feeling all right, Jane?' Smoothly sardonic the voice and quizzing the half-smile he gave her. 'You look tired. Perhaps you didn't sleep?'

'I did sleep!' she replied between her teeth. She was leaving so she had nothing to lose. 'In any case, it's you who ought to have lain awake!'

The grey eyes were suddenly flecked with steel.

'Be careful, my girl,' he warned. 'I don't take insolence from my employees.' He was close and speaking softly so that no one else would hear. In any case, though, there was a great deal of chatter and loud guffaws coming from the table where the men were busy eating.

'I shan't be your employee much longer—' She broke off and gasped as the fat splashed up in the pan and burned her wrist. Scott seemed almost to wince as if it were he who had been subjected to the pain.

'Come and see me at lunch time,' he said. 'I want to have a talk with you.'

'Mrs. Feldwick and Crystal—they'll be there so I—'

'I shall have my lunch brought to my study. It's not a new practice so my visitors won't think it strange.'

She looked at him in some puzzlement, unquestionably at a loss as to why he should want to talk to her.

'There isn't anything to say,' she began then stopped abruptly on hearing his indrawn breath of impatience.

'Do as you're told,' he snapped and turned away. 'Jerry,' he said to one of the men, 'I want you to go over to Jerboa Creek today. They're having trouble with one of the bores.'

'Yes, Boss; I'll ride over directly.'

The chatter died gradually as one by one the men rose from the table and went out. Jane sat down for a few minutes and thanked Anna gratefully when a cup of tea was put before her. She was tired! But she had had little sleep last night—it had been hours before she eventually dropped off—and even then it was a restless sleep she'd had, with continuous tossing and turning, she recalled.

'You have some breakfast?' asked Gelda who was wiping her hands on a clean kitchen towel. 'I'll get it for you.'

But Jane had seen enough of food and she shook her head.

'I'll have a snack presently,' she said and five minutes later she was again in the bath, this time able to take her time and relax. The midday meal was nothing in comparison to the enormous amount of food which Jane had to cook every morning. In any case, she merely prepared the food for lunch and the lubras did the rest, cooking it and serving it.

After the bath Jane busied herself tidying both bedroom and bathroom. Then she dressed, choosing a plain apple green dress of linen, low cut and sleeveless to reveal the honey-tan she was swiftly acquiring. She had washed her hair and she now used the drier to help smooth it and flick up the ends. The unruly quiff brought a sigh from her lips but she had long since become resigned to the fact that it would never do what she wanted it to.

She used the blusher and a hint of lip-rouge, then a rather generous spray of her favourite perfume. She stood before the mirror for a long moment, staring at her image. She knew she was delaying the interview with Scott, but on glancing at her watch she hurried from the room.

She knocked quietly on the door and was invited to enter. Scott was sitting at a large leather-topped desk absorbed in some papers which to Jane's tidy mind looked as if they had been thrown into a waste-paper basket and rescued again. Her office at work had always been well-run and neat; she had known where everything was, her philosophy being that efficiency saved time and was less wearing on the patience than carelessness. And now as her eyes rested on the papers haphazardly scattered over the desk she felt she wanted to set to and put them into some kind of order.

'Have you had your lunch?' was his first question, surprising her.

'No, not yet.'

He gave her a measuring look before saying softly,

'And you've had no breakfast either.' A statement; she coloured a little and said this was true. 'I shall order yours to be brought in here,' briskly as he fingered a bell on his desk. 'We can have it together.'

She said with a hint of suspicion,

'I don't understand, Mr.—er—Boss—' She stopped and pressed her lips together, eyes sparkling. 'I don't understand you,' she repeated. 'If you have something to say to me please say it and let me go. I've no wish to have my lunch with you—as you must very well know.'

He laughed, revealing even, strong white teeth—perfect like the rest of him, thought Jane irritably. Drat the man! If she were granted one wish it would be that he grow a huge wart on the end of his nose! This childish notion brought an involuntary smile of

56

humour to her lips and of course Scott was bound to say,

'What's so funny, Jane?'

'Something I was wish—er—thinking.'

'Wishing, eh?' with a hint of satire that set Jane's teeth on edge. 'Wishing I were a million miles away, no doubt.'

'A little more vindictive than that,' was her instant retort as she reminded herself that she was soon to be leaving this man's employ.

'Indeed? Perhaps you were wishing I were dead?'

She shook her head with instant vehemence and a frown knit her wide, intelligent brow.

'Don't be so hateful! I'm not that bad!'

He laughed and told her to sit down. Her chin lifting at his tone she said tartly,

'I don't want to sit down!' Her blue eyes flashed like chipped ice. 'What do you want to talk to me about?'

For answer he rose from his seat, slowly, almost lazily, but something in the sinuous movements caused her to take a strategic step backwards. His eyes had narrowed but were glinting for all that. He reached her side and she found herself being propelled towards the chair he had previously indicated.

'I—'

'Sit down,' he commanded in a dangerously quiet voice. 'Before I make you.'

Fury brought tiny threads of crimson creeping along the sides of her mouth. Seeing them, Scott pressed a brutal palm against her shoulders and allowed his strong lean fingers to dig into her tender flesh. She found herself helpless beneath the pressure as she was compelled to obey him and sink into the chair. Anger increased to fury but his hand stayed where it was and eventually she leant back, relaxing her stiffened muscles.

'Total obedience is the first thing my employees have to learn,' he informed her as he returned to his own side of the desk.

'I'm leaving!' she snapped.

'When?'

'Just as soon as I can get transport!'

'Which will depend on me.'

She flashed him a look.

'You? You're saying there isn't any transport for me to get?'

'Only if I provide it,' was his cool rejoinder as he pushed some of the papers to one side with the kind of gesture that plainly told Jane that he had no patience with whatever they contained. 'You were a private secretary. I need one and so you will stay.' So coolly authoritative! He might have been a god, she thought, eyes blazing.

'Do you suppose you can dictate to me?' she seethed.

'I need someone like you—' He flipped a hand and frowned heavily. 'This is becoming too much. Take over; you can have the room opposite to this for an office.'

'But—you—'

'Kitchen work doesn't suit you anyway,' he broke in, then looked over her shoulder as Gelda entered after knocking quietly on the door.

'You rang, Boss?'

'When you bring my lunch bring Jane's too—and don't be too long.' Arrogance seemed to make the drawl less apparent and Jane frowned because she did not care for his sharpened tone at all.

She looked at him squarely.

'Mr. Farnham—'

'Boss,' he said curtly. 'No one calls me Mr. Farnham.'

She heaved a deep sigh and compressed her lips.

'I am definitely leaving your employ. You can't force me to stay—no, not even you with your antiquated feudal propensities!'

This obviously amused him because his eyes danced all at once. The change was dramatic, and disturbing to Jane's senses. Why was he so darned attractive!

'You're in a temper and not able to think logically,' he told her after a pause. 'Don't be so hasty, so impetuous. All right, you were weak last night but it isn't the end of the world. Forget it like a sensible girl and begin all over again. I want your services and you want a job— No, don't you dare deny it! You came here with every intention of giving it a fair trial. You told your friend you'd stay initially for a year, and now, because of a little slip, you want to run! Cowardice doesn't become you,' he ended on a stern inflection and she supposed it afforded him extreme satisfaction to see her colour up at his remark.

She sought for words, biting words, but none came, simply because, loathe as she was to admit it, Scott was right. Also, the idea of a change of job was by no means unattractive. Jane saw now what he had been getting at last night when his questions had been so puzzling to her.

The lunch arrived before she could speak; it was on a silver tray which Gelda set down on a table in the window.

'Anything else, Boss?' she asked him with a faint smile on her dusky face.

'Nothing—as long as you've brought the coffee?'

'I have, Boss, in the flask.'

'Thank you.' He flicked a hand and the woman left the room. 'Come on over,' he invited and brought a chair for Jane. She rose with a sigh and took possession of the chair, her mind confused and yet deep in her subconscious she was very sure she would fall in with the plans of the arrogant Boss of Jacana Downs.

The shed dance at Dermot Waters was held less than three weeks after Jane had come to work for Scott Farnham and of course she was invited along with most of Scott's employees for it was traditional that all should have the advantage of what entertainment there was. Jane, settled in her new job, and happy despite the disturbing influence of her boss who now was much closer to her than when she was in the kitchen, was excited at the prospect of attending the dance. It was something new again; she was looking forward to meeting people . . . and she was interested to see what Daphne Woolcott was like.

'I don't know what to wear,' she said to Crystal over dinner the night before the dance. 'Can you advise me?'

'It's informal. I'm wearing a trouser suit of black satin with a white blouse. I shall probably take the jacket off when I get there because you get warm dancing.'

'What are you wearing?' she asked Mrs. Feldwick.

'A dress.' She looked across at her cousin. 'I know it's mostly pants but I'll be all right in a dress, won't I?'

He shrugged indifferently.

'Anything goes from what I've seen.'

Crystal grimaced and later, when Scott had left them on the verandah she said,

'The tough he-man who pretends not to notice what women wear!'

'You mean—he does notice?' Jane did not think so—unless of course it was where his girl-friend was concerned.

'All men notice,' asserted Crystal with conviction. 'But men like Scott with his super-male-ego want to be considered above such frivolities as taking an interest in how women look.' She paused as Jane gave a slight laugh. 'He'll change one day, though, when he's married to Daphne.'

'You seem sure he'll marry her.'

'She's the only one he's been interested in to date. She seems fairly confident—but then she's got so much sex appeal that she can have any man she wants.'

Jane said nothing; her nerves were quivering, for memory had returned, memory of that night when she had come so close to losing herself to Scott. It had never occurred to her that she might also be losing her heart. Even now, when barbs of jealousy struck right into the tenderest spot in her heart, she shirked the analysis of her true feelings. The idea that she had a crush on him had been considered and, squirming at the possibility, she had managed to put it from her mind. But now. . . .

Crystal was watching her intently and with a curious expression in her dark eyes. Jane said lightly,

'I expect the match is very suitable. At least, my friend Margaret said it was.'

Crystal nodded her head.

'Yes, it's suitable. Margaret couldn't stand Daphne, though.'

'Margaret doesn't often take a dislike to anyone.'

'She certainly took a dislike to Daphne. She used to express the wish that someone else would come along and give the girl a bit of competition.' Crystal paused and judging by the sudden gleam in her eyes it would seem that she too disliked the girl who hoped to marry the Boss of Jacana Downs. 'I wonder how she'd react,' murmured Crystal thoughtfully. 'I'll bet she could be a witch.'

'So you don't like her either?'

'Few of the women here do. The men now—they're a different kind of tribe.' Crystal gave a grimace. 'Why do men always go for the veneer? Judgement seems to be beyond them where women are concerned. A pretty face, a bit of flattery and they fall like a heap of bricks tipped off a lorry. Then afterwards they steep themselves in self-pity at the bad bargain they've made. I think I shall leave men alone—die a spinster!'

Jane had to laugh, her eyes appreciative as she took in the youthful beauty of Crystal's face, the slenderness of her figure.

'Want to take any bets?' she challenged and it was Crystal's turn to laugh.

'One has to be so careful these days.' She paused, frowning a little. 'Why has the world changed so much, Jane?' she asked regretfully.

'The world hasn't changed. . . .' Jane's eyes wandered over the verandah rail and the moonlit gardens of the homestead to the scene beyond, a little indistinct in spite of the near full moon, but etched already in her mental vision. The tranquil bushlands where roamed the vast herd of Droughtmaster cattle, the silhouetted MacDonnell Ranges, grey and dun against a purple sky spangled with a billion stars—how impressive and lovely was the Southern Cross! There was magic in the sky and in the earth with their ever-changing shapes and colours; there was mystery in their vastness and the awe-inspiring knowledge that neither could ever be fully understood by man. 'No,' murmured Jane to herself, 'the world hasn't changed, only the people.'

'You're right. But it's so sad. I'm beginning to wish I'd lived in the Middle Ages when people were uneducated but so wise, when they loved one another—' Crystal's voice cut and Jane turned her head in a gesture of enquiry.

'What a serious conversation,' remarked Scott from his place by the open window of the sitting-room. He was negligently leaning against the jamb of the french door, one hand thrust into his pocket while the other fingered his chin thoughtfully. 'Not women's talk, as I'd have expected.'

'We do have some depth to our minds, Scott!' from Crystal tartly. 'What makes you suppose we're all frivolous?'

His brows shot up.

'I wasn't aware that I had given that impression.' He stepped out on to the verandah and spoke to Jane. 'Those accounts I asked you to examine,' he said, 'did you get to the end of them?'

'No, but I hope to do so by mid-morning tomorrow.'

'I've a number of letters I shall want you to take. They're important.'

'You'd like me to take them now?'

He paused a moment then shook his head.

'It's not necessary. But I would like them to catch the mail plane tomorrow afternoon so perhaps you could start work a little earlier.' Although it sounded like a question it was in effect an order. Crystal's eyes darted to Jane's face and then she was glancing up at Scott, an odd expression in her eyes.

'Scott's rather mellow with you, isn't he?' she murmured as soon as he had gone.

'Mellow? I don't know what you mean?'

'He's normally aloof and superior with his employees.'

'Perhaps it's because I'm now his secretary instead of just a home help.'

Crystal shrugged.

'Could be, I suppose. But he never had Margaret eating at his dinner table.'

'Margaret had a friend in the kitchen for company.'
Again Crystal gave a shrug of her shoulders.

'His attitude towards you is very different from
what I've ever seen before with—' She stopped on
seeing Jane's sudden blush. 'I'm embarrassing you.
Sorry. It's just a little puzzling, that's all.'

Undoubtedly she was puzzled, mused Jane a short
while later when she was in her room preparing for
bed. And so was Jane puzzled by Scott's attitude.
Margaret had stressed the fact of his arrogance and
superiority and Jane had come here believing she
would be treated like the servant she was. Perhaps
now she did have a little more prestige but even when
she was working in the kitchen, with the lubras, Scott
had had her dine with him.

Well, as there was nothing to be gained by dwelling
on questions that could not be answered Jane undressed, had a quick shower, and went to bed.

Chapter Four

Scott drove them to the dance in a Landrover, one of several vehicles leaving Jacana Downs for the thirty-mile drive which would bring them to the imposing homestead of Dermot Waters. Jane had decided on a fringed knee-length blue skirt flecked with red and gold, and a matching top in sea-blue chiffon. The neckline was high, mandarin-style, the sleeves long and very full. Jane had wondered if this outfit was just a little too formal but on being shown what Rachel was wearing she had her mind put at rest. A light hand-knitted shawl was draped about her shoulders as she came downstairs, where Scott was waiting at the bottom, superlative in a cream-coloured, casual suit of fine linen with a pale green open-necked shirt. Jane caught her breath at the sheer magnificence of him, so tall and straight, in the very peak of masculine health both physically and mentally. Her thoughts winged to Paddy whom she had believed to be her ideal man. . . . There was no comparison with this paragon, she thought wryly and as a smile curved her lips she saw Scott's eyes flicker, heard him say in that familiar and attractive drawl,

'Why the smile, Jane? Something amused you, has it?'

The smile progressed to laughter and she could not have explained why. Perhaps she was nervous, being watched like this as she came down the wide, balustraded staircase.

'Private thoughts,' was all she said as she took the last couple of steps to bring her to his side. 'Aren't the others down yet?'

'Crystal always takes an unconscionable length of time to get ready and her mother's not much better.' He let his eyes slide over Jane's figure. 'You look charming,' he commented and smiled in some amusement at her blush.

'Thank you,' she returned demurely. 'I wondered at first if this outfit was suitable but Rachel's dress is just as semi-formal.'

'Can you dance?'

'I haven't ever been to a shed dance before. I expect the dances are much faster.'

'Yes, you'll find your energy flagging before the night is out.'

'You dance, Margaret said.'

'Everyone joins in the fun.' His eyes roved again,

this time to settle on the delicate curves of her breasts, accentuated by the cut and fit of the blouse. She looked up to the balcony above the stairs, wishing the others would come.

There was no apology from Crystal or her mother when at last they came sailing down the stairs, two very confident people who would be no strangers to those they would meet tonight—unlike Jane who, although excited and looking forward to the treat, was naturally a little apprehensive at the thought of meeting so many strangers all at once.

Reuben and Allison came along in the Landrover, with Lanky driving the utility which followed closely behind. Sue was with him, and the two sisters from the shop. Paddy One and Two also shared the back of the utility but Jock and the rouseabouts were in another Landrover tailing the utility. The Woolcott homestead was a blaze of lights which could be seen long before the vehicles turned into the long winding avenue of trees leading to the parking space where a number of cars and utilities and Landrovers were already massed.

A few minutes later Scott's party was met by Laura and Francis Woolcott and their daughter. Jane was introduced to them by Scott; she found herself mesmerised by the stunning attractiveness of the girl in white, her gleaming black hair a perfect foil for the beauty of her face. High forehead and widely spaced eyes of darkest brown, a straight classical nose and high cheekbones. The mouth was wide and, thought Jane, just a little too thick-lipped for real seductiveness but there was about the girl a terrific aura of sex appeal; she could never go unnoticed, especially by the male sex! Her figure was perfect, and she knew how to wear her clothes! The bodice of the dress might have been moulded on to her breasts. 'She looks as if she's been *poured* into it,' was Crystal's remark a short while later when she and Jane were talking together.

The hand held out to Jane was cool and smooth; Jane wondered if it had ever dealt with crockery in a sink and decided it had not.

'How do you do?' with a sort of chill politeness as Daphne let her dark eyes sweep with haughty examination over Jane's figure. 'Are you happy in your work at Jacana Downs?'

'Very, thank you,' answered Jane thinking this was not quite what most people would open a conversation with.

'It's hard, though, in a kitchen.' Daphne's eyes wandered to where Scott, hailed by Dick Roberts from Mallee Creek, was standing a few feet away, chatting with him.

Jane was about to inform this arrogant woman that she was no longer in the kitchen when she changed her mind. Let her go on thinking she was a mere menial; someone would eventually put her right!

'What part of England are you from?' inquired Francis politely.

'The Midlands—where Margaret came from.'

'Ah, Margaret. She was very popular here. Everyone liked and respected her.'

Respected. . . . Inwardly Jane was writhing as Scott's words came flooding into her consciousness. It was a most uncomfortable feeling—this sensation of being inferior to Margaret.

'She's getting married, isn't she?' said Laura who, decided Jane, was almost as arrogant and supercilious as her daughter. Francis was very different. A fair craggy man of medium height, he seemed to have acquired a sort of shield which protected him from any barbs and slights his womenfolk might direct at him. Composed and immune, he was able to sail through life on an even keel which all the buffeting in the world could not disturb. He spoke with the familiar drawl but with a deliberation which, thought Jane, was an inherent part of his protective covering. Was he a happy man? Why she should have a question like that come to her mind she could not have explained. But she felt sorry for him even while feeling convinced that he was not a man who needed pity. He had adapted and would survive; he had about him a certain vigour, and a restlessness caused his blue eyes to dart about as if he were searching for something and he knew he would never find it.

Jane liked him but decided she would never understand him, and she doubted anyone else would either.

'What do you think of my cousin's choice?' Rachel was asking when, between dances, she and Jane had found each other in the crowded barn.

'I don't know her well enough to pass an opinion,' was Jane's guarded reply.

'Very tactful. I guess you don't like her any more

70

than we do. I have an idea we shan't be welcome once she becomes mistress of Jacana Downs.' Regret edged the low, musical voice and a shadow rested in her gaze. 'Why couldn't Scott have found someone a little less hard and self-asserted? She's as vain as a peacock, too, inflated with her own attractiveness. Scott must be blind!'

Jane had no comment to make to this, and in any case Jock was by her side, asking her to dance.

'A barn dance, so I hope you've found your breath after the last one!'

'It was a foxtrot. Yes, I have my breath back.'

It was fast and energetic with Jane being whirled about rather more than any other girl on the floor.

'It's not a Scottish reel!' she protested, laughing. 'Jock, have a heart!'

She was flushed and still laughing when at last Jock led her off the floor. Scott was there; he looked down into her happy face with an enigmatic expression and said,

'Watch you don't overdo it. There's a lot to come yet.'

'It was lovely! Such fun!'

'The next is a waltz,' observed Scott and without asking he had an arm about Jane's waist and was leading her back onto the floor. They were on their own for fully thirty seconds with others watching and admiring the way they moved together in perfect harmony. For Jane it was a wonderful experience and a happy one, for she had been conscious of a nagging worry that, should Scott ask her to dance, she would not come up to his standard. Her apprehension had increased as time went on for she felt sure he would soon be seeking her out for a dance.

'You dance superbly,' he commented, his face a little closer to her temple than was necessary. 'You've had plenty of practice?'

'Not plenty. But I belonged to a crowd and we used to go to the local halls and, occasionally, to a dinner dance.' She lifted her face to give him a lovely smile. His grey eyes were immobile and without expression. A tenseness dropped like an all-enveloping curtain around them but they were still swaying and circling in unison and as she slanted an eye, conscious of being on exhibition, as it were, Jane gave a start on noting the expression on the face of the dark-eyed girl standing by the wall, watching them.

Daphne. With narrowed gaze and compressed mouth and a hardness even in the way the high cheekbones seemed to have acquired an added touch of crimson. At the sides of the girl's mouth, too, could be seen dark colour, threads of crimson creeping up and outwards. In a glance Jane noticed all this and she turned again with the swift desire to escape what could only be described as a look of sheer malevolence.

'Something wrong?' Scott was looking down from curious, long-lashed eyes. Others were coming onto the floor and he guided her towards the edge where there was plenty of room still.

'No, nothing,' airily but Jane was still conscious of that stare, burning into her back.

'Those eyes of yours are very expressive,' he observed. 'Something *was* wrong.'

'Nothing of any importance,' she denied, and changed the subject. 'I had a letter from my old employer this afternoon when the mail plane came. He asks how I'm getting along.'

Scott leant away to regard her with a look of sardonic amusement.

'Putting me off, are you? Well, and what do you intend to answer when you write to your old boss?'

She had coloured at his quick perception. He must be curious as to her apparently unnecessary reference to the letter she had received. She wondered what he would say if she were to tell him of that malicious look she had received from his girl-friend, Daphne, who couldn't bear for Scott even to look at another woman, according to what Margaret had written when describing the girl.

'I shall tell him I'm very happy here.'

'And will that be the truth?'

'The whole truth—' She stopped. Was it the *whole* truth? Suddenly all that mattered was the feel of Scott's arm about her, the warmth of his other hand, strong and almost possessive about hers. His lean but hard body and the way he moulded it with hers so that they moved as one . . . so very close as to be intimate. Perhaps it was to be expected that Daphne would resent a pose like this, especially as, for the first half-minute or so she, Jane, and Scott had been the centre of all other eyes. His face too had been close as he bent his head, and even when he lifted it he seemed deliberately to let his chin touch the silken crown of her hair.

'Why the hesitation?' demanded Scott with a touch of authority. 'Finish the sentence.'

'I'm very happy,' she insisted.

'But something's missing.'

'Something is always missing when one is away from one's home,' countered Jane. 'I miss my parents.'

'Your parents,' he echoed in a tone edged with surprise. 'You have parents? Somehow, I gained the impression that you were an orphan.'

'You never asked about my background,' she reminded him.

'No. . . .' He pulled her to one side swiftly as another couple were about to bump into them. Jane missed her step and made an instinctive grab at his lapels. And again her eyes encountered those of her partner's girl-friend. This time the glowering look was more vicious than before. 'Margaret recommended you and that was enough. I didn't even ask for references.'

No. Altogether it had been an unorthodox manner in which she had been given the job, thought Jane and fleetingly her thoughts went to Paddy, who was responsible for her being here at all. How was he getting along? Jane fervently hoped that he was happy now with Mary, just as he was before he met Jane and it seemed that disruption all round would be the result. But Jane had had the sense to pull out in time and she now realised that if she really had been in love with

Paddy she wouldn't have been able to pull out at all since her love would have been stronger than any tugs of conscience. Or would it? Mary was her friend. . . . Questions again which could not be answered and so it was futile to dwell on them.

'Are you ready for something to eat?' Scott asked when presently the music stopped. 'There's barbecued food in the field at the back of the homestead.'

'Yes, I feel a bit peckish.' Why wasn't he with Daphne? Jane glanced around for her as she and Scott came from the shed where the band was beginning to play again.

The chairs and tables were set beneath some Blue Gum trees growing to one side of the homestead, and coloured lanterns had been fixed up among the branches, giving the whole scene an atmosphere of romance. Scott found a vacant table after he and Jane had chosen their food—freshly cooked cutlets and crisp brown sausages with a few garnishings of tomatoes and celery and green peppers. Jane still wondered why Scott wasn't with Daphne and felt half inclined to mention her. However, she had no need, for just as they began eating the girl sailed up, plate in hand, and took possession of a vacant chair at Scott's side.

'Hello,' she greeted them affably. 'I wondered where you'd got to, Scott.'

'We weren't far away—dancing in the shed.' Was there a certain coolness in his tone? wondered Jane flicking him a glance. He was smiling, though, and Daphne was responding.

'Are you enjoying yourself?' The question was put politely and with assumed interest. Jane replied with matching affability.

'Yes, thank you. It's something entirely new. Thank you for inviting me.'

Daphne said nothing and when she did eventually speak it was to Scott.

'Shall you be going into Winangro soon? I'd like to come with you as I've some shopping to do.'

'I had thought of flying in in about ten days or so. What day do you want to go?'

'Any day which suits you,' she purred, touching his sleeve unnecessarily with a slender, crimson-tipped finger.

'A week from Thursday, then?' He turned to Jane. 'Perhaps you would like to join us?'

She gave a small start of surprise but checked immediately and answered with a smile,

'That would be nice. I haven't any shopping to do but I'd like to see the town all the same.'

Daphne said quietly,

'There isn't anything to see. Winangro is nothing more than a few scattered buildings and a couple of dusty streets. I think it would be a waste of time unless you had something specifically to go for.'

'Oh. . . .' Jane felt deflated, conscious of not being able to argue because obviously the girl was right. Scott's mouth was suddenly tight and Jane's eyes widened. She was almost prepared for the curt words that left his lips.

'Nevertheless, the trip will be a change for Jane—a

new experience.' He turned to her. 'Have you flown in a small plane before?' he asked and she shook her head at once.

'No, never.'

'In that case the flight will be something new as well.'

Daphne was staring at him, and it was very plain to Jane that she was controlling herself with the greatest difficulty. Jane felt she would have liked to say something scathing to Scott but instead she managed a smile and the soft and husky purr was in Daphne's tone when presently she said,

'Shall you send someone for me or must I drive myself over to your place?' Her dark eyes seemed soft as a fawn's thought Jane . . . and yet, surely there was a glint of ice within their shadowed depths.

'I'll send Lanky over for you.'

The conversation continued in a rather strained manner for a while and then the three went over towards the crowd milling round the braziers where chicken joints and steaks were still being cooked over glowing charcoal. Jane could distinguish voices—Jock talking to Lanky, and Paddy One chipping in and then giving a loud guffaw; Crystal and her mother chatting to Francis Woolcott; the gruff overtones of Reuben as he carried out an argument with the Woolcott head stockman. Lights flaring from the shed roof and the trees, the amber glow from the braziers, the multi-coloured lamps decorating the eaves of the homestead itself, and the distant lights above, the Southern Cross and the subtler Milky Way streaming out into the boundless maze of infinite. All this spelled novelty and magic for Jane and she gave an involuntary sigh of contentment.

The man beside her turned and slanted her a glance.

'Whatever was that for?' he asked unexpectedly.

She laughed, was aware of the glowering look directed at her by Daphne and was reminded again of Margaret's statement about the girl's jealousy.

'I was so happy—I *am* happy!' She cared nothing for the malicious attitude of the other girl as she spoke with spontaneous frankness to the tall, aristocratic man who had asked the question. 'All this is so wonderful! You know, it's a most apt truism that one-half of the world doesn't know how the other half lives.'

'You're obviously glad you came.'

'Of course. I'd not have missed all this for anything.' Was she being just a trifle catty? Jane asked herself, for she knew just how Daphne was feeling.

'But,' she heard Scott say in a very low voice as he bent his head, 'it's no time at all since you were determined to go home.'

Naturally she coloured, and hoped that the other girl, standing on Scott's right, was unable to see. Certainly she had been unable to hear what he had said.

'I'm glad I changed my mind,' admitted Jane with a little self-deprecating laugh, at the same time marvelling at her instant regaining of her composure after his subtle reminder of the intimacy that had occurred between them. Daphne had stepped forward a pace to speak to her mother and as Jane viewed her in profile she could not help wondering what the girl would think were she ever to know about that intimate scene between the man she hoped to marry and the girl she so obviously disliked. Jane was remembering Margaret's saying in her letter that she would be interested to know what was Jane's opinion of Daphne. Jane knew what she would write in answer to that.

'So am I glad you changed your mind,' was Scott's rejoinder after a small pause.

'You are?' Pleasure brought a delicate wave of colour to her cheeks. 'Er—why . . . ?'

'Because you've turned out to be a very efficient secretary,' was his reply spoken in tones of mocking amusement. 'What other reason would there be?'

Snubbed, she glanced away, and as at that moment Jock turned and saw her, she moved at the same time as he did and within seconds she was being whirled into a barn dance, each succeeding sequence finding her with a different partner. Paddy Two, big and gruff and every inch an Irishman, seemed clumsy after Jock but he was enjoying himself and so Jane bore with him stoically but was glad when the dance was over and she could sit down on the verandah and enjoy the cool breeze. She could see Daphne, still chatting, and Scott was close by her side, one hand resting on her shoulder. Why had he been so cool with the girl? she wondered, and as luck would have it she did have an answer this time to a question she had decided was to remain a puzzle.

'May I keep you company?' Francis Woolcott did not wait for a reply as he sat down beside Jane on the long, cushioned bench. 'Having a nice time?'

'Lovely, thank you. I'm enjoying every minute.'

'But having a rest now, I take it?' His vivid blue eyes darted over to where his daughter was standing with the group of young people. 'How do you like working for Scott Farnham?'

'I'm very happy at Jacana Downs.' Jane spoke non-committally, surprised by the question. 'The house is very gracious and I feel privileged to be living there.' She added this after a pause, feeling she must break the silence without knowing why such awkwardness should prevail.

'Scott and my daughter. . . .' His air of calm was there but Jane felt her nerves tingle because she sensed something dramatic in the atmosphere. He seemed uneasy and anxious, she thought. 'They seem to be all right now.'

'All right?'

'So often they disagree, and tonight Scott's been more inattentive than I have ever known him. . . .' The man paused and his rugged face creased in a frown. Startled by the unguarded way in which he was speaking, Jane merely sat silent, more awkward and uncomfortable than before. He spoke again, a deep sigh in his voice. 'I've set my heart on this match for Daphne, and she wants it too, so why . . . ?' Again he stopped but resumed again almost immediately, 'Why should I be telling you all this?' As Jane had no answer she retained her silence, wishing someone would come along and snatch her away to join in the jig which was being danced at the moment. 'I suppose, young lady, I'm confiding because you're the one who's taken Scott away from her all the evening.'

Staggered now, Jane leant back to regard him with a puzzled expression.

'I haven't been with Scott—Mr. Farnham all the evening,' she denied.

'He's obviously trying to make her jealous.' Francis was speaking to himself, in a very low tone. It was clear that he had not taken any notice of Jane's denial. 'She plays around, making sure he is kept alert to the fact that she can have anyone she chooses and that he's honoured. What she doesn't comprehend is that Scott's no fool and he'll know exactly what she's about, so he retaliates—at least, he has done tonight.' Jane noticed the almost imperceptible pause before he continued, 'People will begin talking and that will really get up Daphne's back . . . if they begin linking his name with yours.'

'Mr. Woolcott,' broke in Jane almost before he had finished speaking, 'you can set your mind at rest on that score! No one is going to link my name with Scott's!'

She was hot all over and had risen to her feet, humiliation engulfing her at the knowledge that Francis had spoken the truth when he maintained that Scott had been trying to make Daphne jealous. So much was explained now; Jane knew why Scott was cool with the girl. She'd been 'playing around' as her father termed it. Jane certainly had not noticed her flirting this evening, so Scott must have been punishing her for something she had done on a previous occasion.

'If you'll excuse me,' she quivered. 'I—'

'You're going? I've upset you?' His face creased; it was all too plain that he had been mumbling to himself and had not really intended embarrassing his companion. 'What a fool I am! I suppose I was regretting the situation that exists between Scott and Daphne. I want this union, my dear—want it more than I have wanted anything in the whole of my life! I like and respect Scott above any man I know. He'd make an honourable and faithful husband to my daughter who, I am sorry to own, needs someone like him to control certain impulses. You see, my dear, she is thoroughly spoiled and pampered; in addition she is beautiful and she knows it. She flaunts that beauty and I am so afraid for her future.' He was baring his heart and uncomfortable as Jane was she felt a surge of pity for him and so she sat down again and turned towards him. He continued, 'Yes, I fear for her future because beauty like hers, and used in the way she often uses it, can bring disaster. Scott would effectively master her, and he's the only man in the Outback who could. She'd not dare flirt or misbehave in any way if she had Scott for a husband.'

'But . . . if she's that way. . . .' Jane let her voice fade to silence, dismissing the idea the girl could be a nymphomaniac. She disliked Daphne but would not brand her as a no-good because of it. She looked at the girl's father, remembering her first impression:

that he was a composed man, able to sail through life on an even keel which all the buffeting in the world could not disturb. She knew he was disturbed at this moment, yet she also sensed the strength almost unimpaired. In short, he was exceedingly anxious for his daughter to marry Scott, but if his wishes did happen to go awry he would recover very quickly, accepting the situation philosophically because that was his nature.

'She's young, I suppose,' he was murmuring to himself. 'So maybe there's some excuse in view of her mother having always spoiled her. She's become headstrong and arrogant, has reached the conclusion that there isn't another girl of Scott's acquaintance whom he would be interested in marrying, and so she believes she has him just where she wants him.'

Jane was frowning, not at all happy at these confidences. She murmured the first thing that came into her head.

'You shouldn't worry too much, Mr. Woolcott. I'm sure it's not as serious as it seems. I can assure you that Mr. Farnham would make sure that his name was never linked with mine. You have to remember that I'm only a servant in his house. He'd be humiliated at such an occurrence just as you and your daughter would—'

'My wife—she would blame me if anything should happen to stop the marriage.'

Jane gave a sigh; he wasn't with her so she was wasting her time trying to set his fears at rest. It hadn't been easy for her to regain her calm after what he had said, and even now she was hot inside, but she had managed to assume a veneer of composure in the hope that she could reassure the man.

'I can't see why your wife should blame you,' she said in a puzzled voice. 'How can it be your fault?'

Francis did not reply but if he had done so Jane felt convinced it would be to say that his wife blamed him for everything.

She looked at him, taking in the ruggedness that made his skin seem perhaps more tough than it really was. It looked like leather. His neck was thick and shoulders broad and giving the impression that he would have no difficulty in throwing a bull when the necessity arose. How had he sired a beauty like Daphne? It was one of the wonders of nature, she concluded.

'I must go,' she murmured, as reluctant now to leave him as she was eager before. Despite the protective cloak she had felt sure he possessed, he did at this moment seem very alone and forlorn. Undoubtedly Scott had spoiled his evening by his cool treatment of his daughter.

He looked at her and said apologetically,

'I oughtn't to have upset you with my problems. Forgive me, my child. It was just a lapse. I felt the need to talk to someone and you happened to be sitting here, on your own.' His eyes darted again to where Daphne was now standing close to Scott, one hand resting on his sleeve. 'I suppose I am worrying unnecessarily, for Scott must see what great benefit it will be if he marries my daughter.'

Jane had risen again and was looking down into his face.

'Excuse me,' she said again and walked slowly along the verandah to where the steps led down to the grassy area below.

Chapter Five

With tears threatening Jane made for the darkness beyond the lights and activity going on around the homestead and the barn. All she wanted was to get away, be by herself to dwell on what Daphne's father had been saying. She had been so happy—apart from the deliberate snub received from Scott, that was—enjoying this new kind of pleasure which was so different from anything she had known before. But now she felt desolate, suffering the pangs of hurt and humiliation which must inevitably result from the realisation that she had been used in order to make Scott's girl-friend jealous. Pride was strong within her, always had been, and now it had been brought to the dust and she felt she hated her employer for the way she was feeling.

She seemed to take a long time in leaving the lights behind her. The chatter became a murmur but then suddenly a discordant laugh broke through it and she frowned as it grated on her ears. She wanted silence and solitude and she began to hurry, desiring only to put a great distance between her and the people who were for the most part still strangers to her. She wished she were back home . . . no, not with things as they were. She could not leave here yet awhile. . . . Her thoughts drifted as she quivered on the brink of apprehension, aware of the spine-chilling sensation which brings the hairs springing erect on one's arms. What sort of a sound was it? Not stealthy footsteps or the snapping of a twig. A thudding? She swung around to scan the starlit landscape. Nothing, and yet she had been sure she heard some sound other than the winging of an insect or the gentle sough of a breeze coming down from the mountains. Woolpacks had gathered to obscure the moon and she had only the light of stars to help her survey her surroundings. No, there was nothing to be seen—unless, she thought, there was something beyond that little copse of gum trees. She decided to turn back and it was at that moment she saw it, an evil black shape silhouetted against the purple background of the night sky. It had come from the other side of the copse. Fear shot through her like an almost physical shock that left her trembling, nerves rioting and a terrible weakness affecting her legs. What ought she to do in this situation? No one had told her—although she had been warned by Scott of these wild bulls. No, she hadn't had any advice as to what she should do if ever faced by a bull. Lie down? That seemed the last thing she ought to do, and yet to run was equally dangerous. It was coming towards her, slowly but in a direct line.

'Oh, God, what shall I do!' And instinctively she screamed. The bull stopped, seeming to slide forward before coming to a complete halt. The scream had cut it short in its tracks; it had also reached the ears of the man who, having noticed a figure hurrying away into the darkness, had been anxiously wondering who it could be.

Scott did not know who he was following, for the vague shape had been well ahead and had disappeared from his view, seeming to merge with the spiky grasslands and scrub. And then he heard the scream and shot forward, skirting the copse to his left.

'Who is it?' he called, then stopped abruptly on seeing the scrub bull. It turned, snorted loudly and then ran off in a direction at right angles to where Scott was standing. 'You damned little fool!' Jane heard him say when he reached her, standing there, paralysed with fear. 'What the hell are you doing out here on your own?'

'I—wanted to—to be—be on my. . . .' Her voice trailed and she started to cry, putting trembling hands to her face as relief, sweeping over her body, left her so weak she was on the verge of collapse. 'I felt the—n-need for peace—'

'And so you wandered off into the bush on your

own, without even telling anyone! You want a damned good shaking!' He looked ready to carry out the threat too, she thought, peering up at his thunderous expression from between tear-damp fingers.

'I didn't think to tell anyone—besides, I'd have looked silly.'

'Not as silly as you'd have looked if the fun had been forced to break up while we all formed ourselves into search parties! You've been warned both about getting lost and about the scrub bulls and you decide to do exactly as you like! Well, miss, you dare to act so imprudently again you'll answer to me! Now, come on—'

'I can't go back like this!' She was seeking for a handkerchief which she had tucked into the waistband of her skirt before leaving home. She had lost it. With an exasperated sigh Scott gave her his own.

'Dry your eyes,' he ordered, then added as if he just had to, 'I've already told you that self-pity bores me!'

Suddenly she was stiff with temper. What right had he to speak to her like this! He had treated her like a child once before, she remembered.

'Then don't stay here and be bored!' she flashed. 'I never asked you to come after me! Here, take this and go!' She actually flung the handkerchief into his face; it dropped to the ground at his feet and she watched, still glowering, expecting him to bend and retrieve it. Instead she heard him say in a dangerously quiet tone,

'Pick it up.'

'Not likely!' she retorted and turned her back on him.

'Pick it up.' Still quiet the voice but something

harsh and frightening made Jane wish to be prudent and do as she was told. Pride, though, remained stubbornly rigid and she heard herself say,

'Pick it up yourself—' And that was as far as she managed to get before, with fingers eating into the tender flesh of her shoulders, she was wrenched around to face him. One hand was all that was necessary to force her to a stooping position where she could reach the handkerchief but, choking as she was with fury, Jane could no more have lowered her pride to obey him than take to the air and fly.

'I'm waiting,' came the threatening tone as the silence stretched and Jane was still being compelled to adopt the stooping position. 'Do you want me to force you to your knees?' asked Scott in what was now an almost languid tone of voice. 'I'll give you ten seconds to obey me and then you'll find yourself in an even more humiliating position.'

She swallowed, aware of the strength of his fingers and that they would be sure to leave bruises which would infuriate her when she examined them later, in her bedroom.

'I—I c-can't,' she said unevenly when the ten seconds were nearly up. 'You asked—'

'No, *you* asked for it—and now you're going to get it.' The same lazy tone but the pressure on her shoulder was increasing. She twisted in a swift and attacking movement hoping to take him by surprise but he anticipated the manoeuvre and she would have been forced right down onto her knees had she not capitulated and reached for the handkerchief.

She gave it to him, heard his mocking comment as he took it from her shaking hand,

'I guess that's the hardest thing you've ever done in your life.'

'I hope you're satisfied!'

'Not quite.' Scott's voice was suddenly as aggressive as the thrust of his jaw. 'I haven't punished you for your defiance.' And with a deftness which took her completely by surprise he had her in his arms, her body crushed against the whipcord hardness of his toughened, sinewed frame. His mouth, moist and sensuous and demanding, possessed hers with a sort of arrogant deliberation designed to let her see that this was indeed meant to be punishment for her rebellious reaction to his order. Lord of all he surveyed, magisterial in his feudal domain of thousands of square miles, he was unused to defiance of any kind and Jane could understand the anger which impelled him to demonstrate his mastery. Yes, she could understand it but that did not prevent her from fighting against it and she struggled fiercely in an endeavour to free herself from the hawsers of steel that imprisoned her.

But she was no match; her efforts were puny and he only laughed at her impassioned diatribe when at last he freed her lips, leaving them bruised and swollen and rosy from the encounter with the sensual domination of his mouth.

He shook her but not roughly and told her to stop feeling sorry for herself.

'You've asked for everything you've been given,' he

added admonishingly. 'Perhaps in future you will think twice before defying me.'

She had reached the state of emotional exhaustion, having to fight not only the wish to repulse him but also the relentless awakening of her own erotic desires. For it was no use denying that his expert love-making and the finesse of experience had been used with calculated persistence in order to bring her to surrender, just as he had once before. The touch of his hands on her breasts, her waist as he spanned it, her thighs when he slid them along in feather-light advances so that she had no control over the spasmodic movement of her body as nerve-stimulation was effected by his easy expertise. He knew it all! Jane wondered how many women had contributed to his knowledge of just how to handle them.

He released her and stood a moment, his mouth curved contemptuously, a flicker of chill amusement in his eyes.

'One day you'll let yourself go,' he said with scorn, 'instead of putting on this "I don't want it" act.'

'You—!' Jane's eyes glimmered in the starlight, smouldering fire in their depths. 'You're rotten!' she flung at him, mindless of any further punishment that could come her way. 'Rotten, do you hear!' she added, almost choked with anger.

'I should imagine they can hear all the way back there,' he said mildly and kissed her again. 'You're darned desirable,' he said throatily, 'are you sure you don't want to—'

'Go to hell!' she gritted. 'I don't know what types

you've been used to, but I *do not* happen to be one of them!'

He seemed faintly startled by her vehemence and stood away as if to regard her from a distance.

'Sorry, then,' he staggered her by saying. 'Maybe I have made a mistake.'

She glared at him, wishing fervently that she had the chance of slapping his face and getting away with it. But she knew otherwise.

'Is the apology supposed to put everything right?' she demanded.

'I suppose you are intending to give in your notice again?' he said with maddening calm as he bypassed her question. 'Well, as I reminded you before, you depend on me for transport. And as I need you as my secretary I can't give you that transport.'

She looked at him challengingly.

'There must be other transport on a huge station like yours,' she said with conviction. 'I notice several of the stockriders own cars. I can ask one of them to take me to the railway station.' She stopped and bit her lip, thinking of Paddy and that it would all begin again once she returned home. In fact, he might just assume she had not been able to keep away from him. She hesitated, loathe to voice what was in her mind but eventually she did. 'If I promise to stay then I want a promise from you,' she began.

'An ultimatum?' All the arrogance of the squatocracy was in his manner. He was the rich patriarchal grazier conscious of his own superiority and power.

'Call it that if you like,' she said with more courage

than caution. 'I know you consider me inferior but you are not my overlord for all that. If I stay I must have your promise that you'll not molest me again.'

'Molest?' with a mocking inflection. 'I'd hardly call it that. You must admit I freed you when you insisted—'

'Oh, be quiet!' she flared. 'Stop laughing at me! I'm willing to stay but only if you give me the promise.'

He did not speak for a space. The clouds had parted to let the moon come through and its argent light was flooding the drowsy landscape. Mountains and low foothills were dark, sleeping monsters, and the trees weird and wraith-like against the mysterious Capricornian sky.

'Something's upset you,' he said unexpectedly. 'That's why you came out here to be on your own.' She noticed the momentary pause and then he added thoughtfully, 'Francis Woolcott was talking to you for some while.' He looked down at her. 'Would you like to tell me what he was saying to you?'

She shook her head, a little too swiftly, her face mirroring apprehension in case he should adopt a persistent attitude and try to make her talk about her conversation with Francis Woolcott.

'It wasn't anything important.'

The grey eyes narrowed.

'In that case,' he remarked at his driest, 'you shouldn't be so worried about repeating it.'

Her eyes darted to his. She drew a deep breath.

'What makes you suppose I'm worried?' she began when she was rudely stopped by his exclamation of impatience.

'Don't prevaricate, Jane,' he admonished. 'You admitted you wanted to be alone so that's why you came out here. And,' he went on deliberately, 'it was immediately after Francis had been talking to you. He seemed to be confiding, to judge by the expression on his face.'

'What he was saying wouldn't interest you.' Jane turned away and began to walk on, towards the homestead, hoping Scott would let the matter drop. Instead, her reluctance merely added fuel to his curiosity; he evidently guessed that Francis had said something which concerned him, but which at the same time had upset Jane.

'You can safely tell me what's troubling you; I'll keep it to myself—' He broke off as she shook her head and impatience drew frown lines between his eyes as he had to increase his pace to match the hurried steps she was now taking.

'I can't tell you. . . .' She felt slightly hysterical, her nerves tensed as a result of her experience with the bull. 'Leave me alone! It was something Mr. Woolcott wouldn't have mentioned if he hadn't been so upset about your—' Too late she stopped, catching her underlip in vexation that she should have been driven by heightened emotion and nerves to let out enough to make it impossible not to enlighten him further. For she felt sure he would coerce her and she was right. He stopped; she was taken roughly by the shoulders and held before him, forced to look into his hawk-like gaze.

'My—what, Jane?' he prompted and she was not deceived by the quietness of his voice. 'He was talking

about me and I demand to know what he was saying.'

She hesitated in spite of the ruthless pressure
increasing as his fingers gripped her shoulders. She
could very well appreciate his frame of mind. He was
not feeling at all comfortable at the idea of Francis
Woolcott discussing him with one of his employees.

'I'm waiting,' he said in the same dangerously soft
tone. 'Don't try my patience again,' he added warn-
ingly and after another slight hesitation she told him
almost all of what Francis had said to her.

'You were using me to make her jealous,' she could
not help adding finally and wrenched herself free.

'So he's worried and he has to confide in a complete
stranger.' Swift fury had erased every other expression from his face. In the dimness Jane noticed the
swelling of a vein in his temple and only then realised
just how strongly affected he was. His pride was
touched; he felt humiliated and she cursed herself for
the original slip which had been the cause of her
having to tell him so much.

'I'm sorry,' she said in a low tone. 'I know how you
feel—'

'You didn't have to listen!' he broke in thunderous-
ly. 'The correct thing for you to do was excuse
yourself and leave him!'

'I'm sorry,' she said again. 'I did intend leaving him
and stood up, but then he began talking again and I
felt so sorry for him that—that I sat down again
and—and listened.'

'Because you wanted to!'

'No such thing! I won't let you accuse me of wanting to pry into someone else's affairs!

'You seem to have learned almost everything about Daphne and me.' He was brooding now but still angry. 'How dared you just sit there and listen?'

Jane's temper flared.

'I've tried to tell you that I wanted to leave him—'

'If you wanted to leave then why didn't you?'

'I'm not continuing with this argument!' she flashed. 'You yourself aren't without blame. You deliberately used me to make her jealous!'

'I did?' The grey eyes were narrowed to slits. 'You take a lot for granted.'

She blinked at him.

'It's true,' she began. 'You've been with me quite a lot this evening.'

A strange silence followed, unfathomable and lengthy. And as Jane stared up into his mask-like face she became conscious of vibrations affecting her nerve-ends. This brooding silence—what did it mean?

'The fact that I have spent some time with you,' he said at last, 'does not mean that I had some ulterior motive.'

'Then what . . . ?' She was embarrassed by the idea that had entered her head. She saw his lip curve in a sardonic smile as he said,

'Yes, you are right. I might have been with you for the very simple reason that I liked your company.'

A soft and delicate tinge of colour came to her cheeks and she wondered if he could see it as he stood there towering above her in the moonlight.

'You're an enigma,' was all she could find to say because she was now recalling his coolness and his snub.

'That makes two of us, Jane.' He was regarding her now almost with indifference but his brow was creased in thought. And then, out of the blue, and staggering her into speechless disbelief, he said quietly, 'Would you consent to becoming engaged to me, Jane?'

It seemed an eternity before the silence was broken, and even then it was by Scott, for Jane felt she had surely imagined the question he had put to her so calmly and with that soft inflection which took out every bite that had been there before.

'I'm serious, Jane. It would be a sham, of course, but it would serve a purpose I have in mind.'

At last she was able to say, freeing herself from his hold,

'It's the craziest idea I've ever heard. A sham engagement? How melodramatic can you get!' She felt slightly hysterical again, this time the result of this fantastic situation and the incredible composure of the man who had just made the preposterous suggestion without even thinking to explain why.

'You'd not lose by it,' he promised her in the same tones of studied indifference. 'I shall pay you for the—er—service.' Amusement edged his voice as he added before she could speak, 'I have never yet met a woman who couldn't find a use for extra money.'

She lifted her chin at that but had no retort ready. In fact, she was becoming aware of some mysterious and compelling force telling her to consider his proposal. Staggered and baffled she attempted to analyse her feelings, to find some reason why she should be considering the matter at all. Could it be because she knew in her heart that Daphne was not right for Scott? Or could it be that she herself could not bear the thought of the two becoming man and wife? That Scott's masculine attractions—his lean good looks and perfect physique—affected her profoundly she could not deny, and she had to admit that, deep in her subconscious, she had cherished the hope that Scott would notice her as a woman.

She said at last, looking up intently into his eyes,

'You have a reason, obviously?'

'Obviously,' he agreed with disarming mildness, 'but that need not trouble you. Is it that you are considering my proposal?'

She shook her head but it was not a negative gesture. This ferment of emotions, the vague and misty state of her mind. . . .

'I can't think clearly!' she complained, glaring at him as if it were all his fault—which of course it was, she told herself. 'Why can't you give me the reason? Everyone believes you're almost engaged to Daphne.'

'That's just it,' was his casual rejoinder. 'I suppose,' he added with a touch of asperity, 'I must give you some explanation.'

'Even if you do it's no guarantee that I shall fall in with your offer.' She stopped and there flashed before her mind the reaction of other people on the station. 'It's impossible,' she said decisively. 'Everyone would be astounded.'

His innate arrogance came to the fore, revealed in his eyes and in the tautened line of his jaw. Every inch the aristocrat, thought Jane and wondered what his original background was—the nobility of England?

'I am not in the least interested in the opinions of others,' he snapped.

A law unto himself, she mused wryly as she met the arrogance in those steely grey eyes.

'Well, perhaps you will give me your reason?' invited Jane, gradually recovering from the shock of his proposal. She was curious to hear what he had to say even though some little access of perception was telling her that he had no intention of providing her with the *real* reason for wanting her to become engaged to him.

'I am not intending to pander to the whims of the match-makers.'

Her eyes flickered as she pondered this.

'And who are the match-makers?' she inquired gently.

'Francis Woolcott and his wife, mainly.'

'He's upset,' she began. 'It's a shame to hurt him any more than he's hurt already. He wants the match.' She stopped and frowned, confusion sweeping over her. Surely she was not trying to persuade Scott to marry the girl just to please her father!

'He's hurt only because of the possibility of the two estates not being joined.' Scott seemed to be speaking to himself; he was distant and aloof suddenly and she waited for the mood to pass. 'Well—' He brought his full attention back to her. 'What is your answer?'

'How long is the engagement to be for—' She broke off, telling herself it was sheer madness to fall in with a plan that would inevitably bring her into closer contact with Scott . . . when she could be in great danger of becoming so emotionally involved that lasting hurt could be the result. And yet the idea was tempting, for there was always the possibility—remote, it was true, she had to admit but there all the same—that he would fall in love with her.

The thought instantly led to another, that of whether she really wanted him to fall in love with her.

She nodded slowly as full perception dawned. *She* was in love with *him* already. . . .

Her decision was made easy but even as she gave him the answer he wanted she knew a stab of fear that the end of it all would be heartache for her.

'Thank you,' he responded casually. 'As I've said, you will not lose by it. I shall pay you well.' He paused in thought. 'You've asked how long the engagement will last. That all depends on certain circumstances.'

'And those are?'

'I can't tell you,' he replied firmly.

'I have a right to know!'

'Someone else is involved,' he almost snapped, 'and for that reason I cannot enlighten you further.' Inflexible the tone to match the expression in his eyes. Jane bit her lip in vexation but refrained from asking any further questions that in all probability would end in her being snubbed.

Chapter Six

Jane was strolling in the garden, stopping now and then to watch the flock of galahs, forming a pink and grey cloud as they flew from one tree and settled, and from that tree to another. The roseate cockatoo was its name in England and Jane could recall seeing these in the zoo at Chester. But it was much nicer to see them in the wild, she thought, a smile coming to her lips and hovering there.

Suddenly she was aware of someone behind her and before she turned she heard Sue's cheery voice.

'Hi there, Jane.' But then Sue seemed to take on a more respectful manner . . . almost deferential and it brought a swift frown to Jane's forehead.

'Hello, Sue. It's obviously one of your days for coming in. . . .' Her voice trailed and her frown deepened. She had been about to say that it was one of Sue's days when she came to do some cleaning at the house.

'Awkward, isn't it?' perceived Sue on noting the discomfiture of the girl who had fast been becoming her friend. Now, though, with her being engaged to the Boss things were not quite the same. 'You've taken several steps up while I have stayed where I was.'

'Don't!' exclaimed Jane in distress, 'We're still friends and always will be.'

'You'll be the wife of my husband's employer.' Sue had a large basket over her arm; she was on her way to the vegetable plot where she would collect the vegetables wanted for dinner and then go back and prepare them, to be cooked later by the lubras. 'It makes a difference, Jane, no matter what you say or what protests you make. The Boss wouldn't care for his wife to be a bosom friend of the wife of one of his stockmen.'

'Stop!' protested Jane almost in tears. She felt so ashamed at the deception, wondering what Sue would think if and when it came to an end.

If. . . . With a sigh Jane watched Sue walk on, swinging the basket in her hand now in a careless manner as if she were telling herself that it did not matter that the friendship must come to an end.

'Hello, Jane.' Crystal came up a few minutes later, when Jane was standing by the pool, pensively staring down into the blue water. 'Thinking of going in for a swim?'

Jane shook her head.

'I don't feel like it.'

Crystal, in shorts and a sun top, looked at her with a sidelong and perceptive glance.

'Something's wrong, isn't it, Jane?'

'No—er—what makes you ask that?'

'You don't act at all like the starry-eyed fiancée of one of the most eligible bachelors in the Outback—*the* most eligible bachelor, in fact.'

'I'm very happy,' returned Jane with a forced smile. 'It's wonderful to—to be engaged to Scott.'

Crystal continued to subject her to an intense scrutiny.

'It was so sudden—no one so much as noticed that you two were even all that friendly, much less in love.'

Jane had nothing to say. After a week she was still in a daze, wondering what had made her agree to this deception, wondering too just what the real reason for it could be.

She recalled the amazement when, just before the shed party broke up, Scott, with an arm about her shoulders, asked for silence as he had something to say. Jane, crimson, and with her heart slamming against her ribs, had wished she could be swallowed up where she stood. Nerves were rioting and at that moment she felt she almost disliked the man responsible for her discomfiture. He was so calm and collected, without a muscle stirring in his mask-like countenance.

'Jane and I have just become engaged to be married.'

The gasp that went up could scarcely be described as tactful, but as everyone had a shock it was not surprising that reaction was uncontrolled. Jane had glanced from under her lashes at Francis Woolcott; his face had gone a sickly yellow while his wife, standing beside him in readiness to say good night to the departing guests, seemed as if she had been turned to stone. Daphne. . . . Jane could shudder even now as she recalled the undisguised hatred after the dilating of Daphne's eyes in disbelief. Swift and heavy colour had flooded her cheeks and her hands had clenched at her sides.

And then, as murmurings broke out at last, the girl sauntered over and with a smile on her lips she had said with a clarity and calm that amazed everyone present,

'Do accept my congratulations, Scott, Miss Talbot —I hope you'll be happy.' So gracious, thought Jane. The result of good breeding. But how did she feel beneath the veneer? That she must be seething was evident from that first unguarded moment after the announcement had been made by Scott, staggering every single person present.

People had then begun to surge forward to add their good wishes to those expressed by Daphne, but Francis Woolcott and his wife never moved, and the unhealthy yellow colour on Francis's face was now a dull grey and his eyes looked very tired.

Yet he would rally, decided Jane as she recalled her

initial impression of his character. This was not the first blow he had suffered in his life. He had come through before and he would again.

Jane had sat beside Scott in the Landrover on the way back to Jacana Downs and asked herself: when this engagement is broken will he go back to Daphne? For some reason known only to himself he was taking a course which was only temporary, so what were his plans for later on?

'You're very quiet.' Crystal's soft voice recalled Jane and she gave a small sigh. She felt like confiding and wondered if she dared. She did not know Crystal too well but already they were friends—'kindred spirits' asserted Crystal.

'I was thinking,' admitted Jane when Crystal moved to remind her she was awaiting a response to her remark.

'Regretting?'

Startled, Jane widened her eyes.

'Why should I regret anything?' she demanded.

'I know this seems over-familiar,' said Crystal after a pause, 'but I believe you are play-acting, Jane.' She looked at her squarely as Jane turned her head. 'Mother is of the firm opinion that this engagement isn't genuine.'

Silence. Jane could not have lied successfully so she said nothing.

And at that moment Scott himself appeared, having ridden up to the front of the homestead on his magnificent chestnut gelding which he handed over to the roustabout who had come hastening up. With long lazy strides Scott reached the two girls, his narrowed eyes moving, from one to the other. Jane averted her head but knew full well that he had seen her heightened colour. Crystal looked faintly uncomfortable in face of this unexpected encounter but she soon recovered to put on a cool, collected front.

'Confidential talk?' Scott stood towering there, feet slightly apart, hands tucked into his belt, his slouch hat tipped back to reveal hair slightly bleached at the front.

'Not at all,' answered Crystal, smiling. 'We were just saying how lovely the gardens are with the flowers and smooth lawns and the statuary. The poinciana trees are just marvellous, and the hibiscus and oleanders. What are those over there—?' Crystal pointed to a little grove bordering the farthest corner of the grounds. 'I don't know their name.'

'Bauhinia trees,' he replied smoothly. 'I haven't noticed you take so much interest in trees before, Crystal,' he added and Jane looked up. His eyes met hers; she wondered what he read and a swift sigh escaped her. If only she could set the clock back. . . .

'One should always be interested in trees,' responded Crystal in the same unruffled voice. 'Take them away and man's potential is seriously endangered.'

'I agree,' he nodded. 'Plants and animals are vitally necessary to one another.'

'I think I ought to go and see what Mother's doing,' decided Crystal after a pause. 'I left her trying to sew a zip fastener in a skirt and she was grumbling that I wouldn't help her.' She cast Scott a glance. 'How can two people sew in one zip?' Without waiting for an answer she went off, leaving Jane in a situation she would much rather have avoided.

It was no surprise when Scott with his innate perception asked what Crystal had been saying that had caused Jane such obvious embarrassment. She looked at him a moment in indecision and then said resignedly,

'I don't suppose it matters if you know. In any case,' she added with a tart inflection, 'if I don't tell you you'll make me.'

He laughed and said, 'That was a little mixed, wasn't it? Well, what was Crystal saying to you?'

'She and her mother think the engagement's not genuine.'

His eyes flickered but otherwise he gave no indication of having been affected in any way by this piece of news.

'And what did you say to that?' he wanted to know, absently taking off his hat and holding it in his hand.

'I didn't say anything. I couldn't have lied to her.'

'My appearance was timely, then?'

'Yes, it was.'

He came closer to her and stared down into a face that was still a trifle pink.

'It would seem a demonstration of our affection is necessary.'

She gave a start and shook her head.

'That isn't funny,' she retorted.

'It wasn't meant to be. On the contrary it was meant to be serious.' He glanced around. 'I rather think Crystal—and perhaps her mother—are interest-edly watching, and so—' With a little tug of her wrist he had drawn her close; she began instinctively to struggle and was ordered to stop: 'You're defeating the objective!' he added and, bending his head, he locked his lips to hers.

Chapter Seven

Someone else involved. . . . Scott's words came back with almost monotonous repetition and by the time Thursday came along Jane felt she would not be able to contain her curiosity any longer. She was in the airplane, looking down at a mob of kangaroos and several times since the moment she and Scott were airborne the question had come to her lips, only to be stifled because she feared a snub from her companion. Daphne had sent word that she did not wish to go into Winangro and neither Scott nor Jane was surprised, although neither said anything to the other about it.

'You're very quiet.' The silence was broken at last. Jane said she was absorbed by what was going on down below.

'It's all new as yet, remember,' she added.

'Winangro will also be new,' he commented with a trace of amusement, 'but I doubt you'll think much of it.'

'A dusty town at the end of a railroad track,' quoted Jane catching his humour. 'At any rate, it will be a novel experience and something to talk about when I go back home.'

He turned to slant her a glance. She saw his expression and it seemed that, inwardly, he was frowning.

'You're thinking of the time when you'll be leaving here?'

'Not consciously,' she mused. 'To tell the truth, I can't imagine being back in England. It's become so remote.'

'It is remote.'

'In miles, yes,' she agreed. 'But, somehow, it's becoming vague as well—as if I've been here for years.'

He smiled strangely and let that pass without comment. He was looking down and said after a while,

'That's Sandalwood Downs Station, owned by the great-grandson of Phoebe Bancroft. She was a character if ever there was one!' He paused a moment and it seemed that his mouth went tight as if he were recalling something unpleasant.

'You know her great-grandson?' asked Jane and he nodded at once.

'A nice guy,' he answered almost to himself. 'And a fool—' Scott broke off abruptly and then changed the subject. 'Have you some shopping to do in Winangro?

I ask because my own business will take about two hours, perhaps a little more so you'll be on your own.'

'I'll find something to do,' she assured him. 'I don't really have any shopping—unless one can buy souvenirs?'

'Depends on what you want. You can buy paintings by Aborigines and some are very fine indeed.'

'I'll take a look,' she said. She could still see the low, red-roofed homestead of Sandalwood Downs Station, and a great mob of cattle grazing the wide rangelands and the low hills beyond the spinifex plains. Something made her say,

'What is the name of Phoebe's great-grandson?'

He turned swiftly.

'Elliot Bancroft.'

'Tell me about Phoebe,' she invited.

He turned again, his attention with the controls.

'You really want to know about her?' he asked presently.

'Yes; she sounds intriguing.'

'She was intriguing, although many other wives of pioneers had the same courage and grim determination to win out against the numerous hazards of this unfriendly land.'

'It must have been tough in those early days.'

'It was.' Scott became thoughtful for a space and then, 'Phoebe was ninety-five years old when she died, and, therefore, many of us can still remember her. She should have had a pair of spurs cemented into her headstone. She lived for the saddle until the day she could not mount a horse no matter how hard she tried. She came here with her parents when she was fourteen. They all came with a band of settlers whose optimism outweighed their commonsense. They lived in huts and began to raise cattle. Phoebe and other females had to carry water from a lagoon half a mile away—carried it on a yoke. Commodities came by camel team and the nearest post office was four hundred miles away; you got there on horseback as there was no other form of transport. They lived on dry bread and meat, year in and year out. Phoebe married young and raised nine children in between helping on the station. She wore rough riding breeches and an enormous slouch hat.' He paused a moment and Jane said in a voice edged with admiration,

'She sounds terrific—a legendary character whose name will never die.'

'She could break brumbies and throw steers as well as any man. Mustering and branding were in a normal day's work—and all this in addition to bringing up those children. She was just about as tough as it was possible to be. She was known on one occasion, when her husband was ill, to do the droving—eight hundred miles she walked and was away for months.'

'She drove the herd of cattle through the wilderness for all that way?' The awed disbelief in Jane's voice brought a fleeting smile to her companion's lips.

'Seems impossible? I suppose it does to a modern miss like you. There's no stamina in the young today,' he added and in his tone there was something akin to contempt. 'None of us would be here now but for those courageous pioneers who never accepted defeat.'

'The water, for the cattle and the drovers,' said Jane. 'How did they get water in the desert?'

'It was pumped up by hand from the wells.'

'By hand. . . . For all those cattle.'

He nodded and went on, 'There were dust storms, wild bulls, danger from Aborigines who attacked with deadly spears and there were droughts.'

'It's a wonder anyone survived.'

'They did, though, building up their stock from a few dozen to hundreds and then, with the passing of a generation, to thousands and this is our heritage. Every one of us has these pioneers to thank.' So serious the tone and the delivery of the words. Jane was learning something new all the time about the man to whom she was 'engaged'.

And what she was learning was too attractive by far! She had no illusions about the man . . . or about her own vulnerability to his charm. She marvelled that Daphne, with the chance of winning him for her husband, could run risks of losing him by acting the way she had.

She said after a small silence, and as the Bancroft homestead was becoming indistinct, a mere dot on the landscape,

'How many cattle does Elliot Bancroft have today?'

'Over twenty thousand, at a guess.'

'The mind boggles,' she said and then felt sure that Scott owned far greater a number than that of his friend. But he merely nodded and for the rest of the flight there was silence in the airplane.

And then they were landing, smoothly, onto the strip.

'I'll meet you outside the bank,' he said as they prepared to go their separate ways. 'And we'll have a snack in the café over there. It doesn't look much but the food's excellent.'

Jane watched him stride away to mingle with others of his kind—flint-hard men of whipcord strength and muscle, men more at home in the saddle than in the soft luxury of an armchair or a sofa.

She wandered along the dusty street, pleasantly surprised that the tiny town was bright with an abundance of poinciana trees and bauhinias. Yes, the street was dusty and the shops were surprisingly smart and clean, with bright paint and rather gay sunblinds. Some dusky children played on the corner and Jane was later to learn that, in the old days, Aborigine children attending the school had caused animosity and protests from the parents of white children who maintained that as the Aborigine children slept with dogs they were liable to carry disease to school. Now, though, there were no such petty objections and blacks and whites attended school together.

As time went on a fierce sun intensified the heat and Jane was thankful for the hat which Scott told her to bring with her. She discovered the shop selling the paintings and found one which she liked very much—a scene of heat and dust, with a forlorn near-dead mulga tree as a prominent centrepiece and starkly on its leafless branches were the skulls of a horse and a cow.

'It's symbolic of what the wilderness can be,' the salesman explained and although she had her doubts about Scott's liking the painting, Jane decided to buy it. Only then did she ask herself why she should have brought Scott into it. After all, it would not be hanging in *his* house.

The painting was fairly large so Jane asked if she could leave it for a while. She would collect it, she thought, on the way back to the plane.

She arrived at the meeting place a few minutes early and was glad because Scott was already waiting.

'I'm sorry,' she began but he interrupted her at once.

'Don't apologise; I'm early.' He looked her over. 'Enjoyed yourself?' he asked with a hint of humour in his voice.

'Yes, as a matter of fact, I did.' She paused a moment. 'I bought a painting.'

'You did? Where is it?'

'At the shop. It's rather large so I thought I'd collect it later.'

'We'll have that snack,' he said and with a hand beneath her elbow he ushered her across the road. The unexpected action made her feel warm and happy. The sensation of his nearness made her heart jerk a little, pleasurably. She was recalling his saying that he might have been with her at the barbecue because he enjoyed her company. Now, as they entered the café she glanced up at his profile and found the austere lines appearing to be a little relaxed, just a tiny bit softer, and somehow she knew he was enjoying her company at this moment.

But enjoying a person's company was no guarantee of any deeper feelings, Jane told herself admonishingly. She was allowing her hopes to soar just because he had taken her arm to guide her across the road!

The flight home was over the same territory but now the Bancroft homestead was in shadow for the sun was setting behind the low hills at the back of the cluster of buildings, and even the cattle were dark shapes moving sluggishly across the drowsy landscape. A region of sparse mulga had been left behind, its monotony relieved only by the sporadic appearance of ghost gums depicting the presence of a dry watercourse. Now, though, the habitation of Sandalwood Downs Station was a dramatic change and as she looked down Jane kept thinking of Phoebe Bancroft and others like her whose determination and grit were responsible for these massive Outback estates.

'Was Elliot Bancroft at the Woolcott's party?' she asked without quite knowing why.

'No,' came the brief reply and Scott's voice seemed to be curt almost to the point of harshness.

'I shouldn't have asked?' Again she had no idea what had prompted such a question.

'It doesn't matter.' He fell silent for a long while and she guessed he was considering . . . what? He said after a space, 'You seem curious about Elliot?'

'I don't know. . . .' She hesitated. 'I sense a mystery.' She looked at him, saw the half-smile touch the corner of his firm mouth. She saw the crinkly lines spreading, fan-wise, from the corners of his eyes and thought how very attractive they were, giving evidence of the outdoor life he led because they were caused by the continual narrowing of his eyes against the relentless Capricornian sun.

'A mystery, eh?' Scott nodded as he spoke. 'It isn't a mystery, really, but it may seem like it to you.' He became thoughtful and she knew he was again pondering. At last she heard him say, 'Eliott's the other person who's involved.'

'He is?' Jane's eyes opened wide. 'But how—I mean, in what way?'

'He happens to be in love with Daphne—madly in love.' Scott's voice was grim and faintly scornful. 'He's crazy about her and, I have to admit it, he's right for a woman like Daphne.'

'Right? Is he—er—masterful?'

Scott looked at her slantways and laughed.

'What makes you suppose she needs someone masterful?'

'Her father told me so.'

'But he said that she and I were suited.'

'That's right.' She knew where all this was leading but was unable to sidetrack him.

'And are you saying that I am masterful?'

She was honest, saying yes, she did think he was masterful.

'I suppose you have to be assertive,' she added before he could speak, 'because of having to run such a vast estate where so many people are employed.'

'Assertive. . . .' He shrugged his broad shoulders. 'Genetics,' he decided suddenly. 'My father was a most domineering man.'

'And you admit you take after him?'

'I suppose so,' was his casual rejoinder.

118

'We seem to have bypassed the subject that brought all this about,' she said.

'Elliot? The reason why I became engaged to you was to see if he stood a chance with Daphne. I have an idea she will now agree to marry him.'

'In effect,' mused Jane with a slight frown, 'you've stepped down in favour of your friend?'

'Exactly.'

'Is it fair—?' She cut abruptly, colouring up.

'You obviously don't think much of Daphne,' he stated with a quirk of amusement. 'You're sorry for Elliot!'

'I shouldn't have said it,' she apologised. 'I scarcely know the girl.'

'Daphne's pretty transparent to anyone with average intelligence.'

'You feel that—well—she could make Elliot a good wife?'

Scott laughed at the sceptical tone in which she spoke.

'You haven't much confidence,' he said.

'It has nothing to do with me.' Jane glanced down, her attention caught by a mob of kangeroos grazing where the cattle had been. They sometimes appeared almost grotesque in the constantly changing colours created by the lowering of the sun.

Another homestead appeared in her view and she asked Scott about it and who lived there.

'It's Lake Togo Downs. You met the Southerbys—Felicity and Sam. They inherited the station from Sam's uncle who died at eighty-seven. He'd started with a small herd of breeders and lived in his swag and an old tin shed for several years until he at last began to make money. You can see the changes that have taken place over the years.'

'Yes, indeed.' The white homestead was surrounded by lush green lawns and what seemed to be luxurious shrubs. 'Is that a citrus grove, over to the right of the house?'

Scott nodded.

'A very large one. And you can see the lake after which the station's named.'

'It looks lovely.' The waters of the lake shimmered with a golden light reflected from the sun-tinged hills above and to the east of the homestead.

Scott pointed out such things as the fattening paddocks, the paddock where the brumbies were broken, and she frowned then and said with an edge of sadness not unmingled with protest,

'Do they have to bring in the lovely wild horses and tame them?'

'Of course. We need horses.'

'You could breed all you need.'

'We do breed some, but—well—' He pointed suddenly and his voice was vibrant with eagerness. 'Just as it happens there's a beauty! He's too clever, though. He escapes every time Sam tries to capture him.' The brumbie was standing proudly on a small rise, a glorious mane flowing, the head held proudly, the splendid body motionless.

'I hope they never manage to capture him!'

Scott laughed.

I rather think you'll have your wish,' he said and

she found herself releasing a breath. 'As I've said, he's managed for a long time now to remain free and I reckon he always will remain free.'

'He deserves to.'

'I agree, in a way. Nevertheless—' Scott broke off as the brumbie turned as if at some sound and then raced away, fast as the wind. 'Nevertheless, I'd not mind owning an animal like that.'

'No one should own him!'

Again he laughed, slanting her a glance.

'I guess that if you had any say you'd not allow any wild horse to be captured and tamed.'

'You're right; I wouldn't!'

No more was said until they were landing on the Jacana airstrip when Jane said with a smile,

'Thank you, Scott, for taking me. I enjoyed the flight very much, and the town was a novelty.'

'I must try to take you to Alice Springs sometime,' he said, surprising her. 'You'd really enjoy that.'

Len, the jackeroo, was at the airstrip within seconds, driving the utility.

'I saw you coming in to land, Boss, and so I brought the ute out for you.'

'Thank you, Len.'

'Had a good trip, Boss?' Len waited until they boarded the vehicle then slid behind the wheel again. Young and still 'raw' Len was an apprentice cattleman taken on by Scott a few weeks previously. Jane had learned that a jackeroo usually lived in at the homestead of his employer and ate at his table, but Len had made friends with a young couple living in one of the bungalows and had asked if he could accept their offer

121

of accommodation. When eventually Len was a fully trained cattleman he would probably move to the men's quarters—and often eat his meals sitting on his swag. It often depended on where a man happened to be; the rangelands were so vast that stockriders could be away from civilisation for weeks on end.

A tough life, mused Jane when, later, she was at her bedroom window staring out into the darkness of a warm and balmy night. Men here were so different from those whose lives were lived out in big towns and cities where everything science could invent was laid on for them. Here, in this Never-Never land of limitless spinifex plains, of billabongs and dried-up river beds, men had adapted to a gruelling life of hard work where the determination to survive was paramount, for if this land were to be neglected for even a short time it could easily revert to its original, primordial state.

Jane felt its pull already, its strange mystery and magnetism . . . and she felt also the pull of the man to whom she was engaged.

The thought of leaving here, ever, was so dismaying that she refused to dwell upon it.

However, she did eventually find herself dwelling on several other things, one of which was the suspicion of Crystal and her mother that the engagement was not genuine.

What were they going to think when eventually it came to an end? Well, decided Jane with a sigh, it was Scott's problem not hers and she did not doubt that he would deal with it in his usual efficient way.

Chapter Eight

It was the evening of a film show and buffet given by Scott and most of the people Jane had met at the Woolcott shed dance had put in an appearance at Jacana Downs, including the Woolcotts . . . and Eliott. Jane took to him instantly and felt faintly depressed at the idea of his getting anyone like Daphne for a wife.

'He's crazy about Daphne, isn't he?' Crystal was beside Jane and there was a slight frown on her face. 'She attracts the men like a honeypot attracts flies!'

Jane was watching the handsome young man as he hovered around the beautiful Woolcott heiress. She in turn seemed interested in him but somehow Jane was of the opinion that it was all a pose, that she was striving to give the impression that she couldn't care less that Scott was engaged to someone else. Her smile for Eliott was charming and it did at times seem to carry a hint of affection which caused the young man to beam with satisfaction and pleasure.

'Just how deep is the friendship between Scott and Eliott?' inquired Jane of her companion. The film show had finished and now everyone was standing about in groups, having drinks before the buffet was uncovered by the two lubras whose task it had been to prepare it. It was on a long table in the dining-room of the homestead but the drinks were being taken outside, on the verandah or the terrace where small tables and chairs had been placed in groups. A few more were on the lawn and some even by the pool patio. Daphne and Eliott were in a group of young people including Felicity and Sam Southerby, and Scott. Daphne looked superb in a trouser suit of green satin trimmed with glittering sequins; she wore diamonds at her throat and in her ears. Poised and confident, a clever conversationalist and an expert at using eye-catching mannerisms, she seemed to be holding her small company spellbound and Jane as she watched wondered even yet again how Scott could have resisted her. Yes, since her engagement she had thought often about this, feeling puzzled that Scott had not grasped the chance of a beautiful wife and the vast estate she would eventually inherit.

'I don't really know,' Crystal was answering slowly and thoughtfully. 'I do know that Scott has a great admiration for him and the way he runs the estate.'

Jane sipped her drink, very conscious of the diamond and sapphire ring she wore on her engagement finger. She felt an imposter, duping all these people— But no. It was Scott who was duping them! Jane was not going to blame herself like this.

'I wonder. . . .' she murmured almost inaudibly.

'Wonder what?'

'If they'll—well, get together.'

'Now that she can't have Scott, you mean?' The strange quality of Crystal's voice gave indication of doubts still being with her regarding the genuineness of the engagement. This despite the fact that Scott now always seized every opportunity of displaying affection, for the benefit of his cousin and her daughter, he said . . . but Jane had begun to suspect that he rather enjoyed kissing and fondling her, which was usually in the darkness of the garden, after dinner when he had suggested a stroll, and when he knew that the two women would be watching from the verandah or from the window of the living-room, whichever place they happened to be at the time.

'He's nice,' was all Jane said in response to Crystal's words.

Crystal was silent and thoughtful, sipping her iced lemonade and fixing her eyes on Eliott's bronzed and handsome face.

'Yes,' she agreed at last, 'he's nice—far too nice for her.'

'I think so, too. It will be a shame if he does get her for a wife.'

'It isn't as if he's interested in her money,' said

Crystal in a low and brooding tone. 'You can see he's madly in love with her.'

'She's so charming—outwardly.'

'Why can't men look deeper than the surface?'

'It's a question that's been asked a million times, must have been. Undoubtedly a pretty face and figure are all that attracts a man initially.'

'They deserve all they get,' was Crystal's rather vehement rejoinder. 'I don't know why you should feel sorry for Eliott, for I'm sure I'm not!'

'You . . . ?' Jane turned slowly to regard the girl who had become her friend. 'I don't understand,' she murmured, but it was only for something to say. She felt she did understand. . . .

'What don't you understand?' Crystal was tilting her head as if she were puzzled by Jane's remark. 'There's nothing *to* understand.'

'No . . . of course not. . . .'

Jane was saying to Scott a short while later as they stood side by side at the buffet table,

'Do you suppose there's really any possibility of Daphne and Eliott getting together?'

'I should say there's every possibility.'

'And you feel satisfied?'

He looked down into her face, puzzled by her query.

'Why do you ask a question like that?' he wanted to know and saw Jane make an impatient gesture with her hand.

'You became engaged to me to make the way clear for Eliott,' she almost snapped.

'What of it? I know just how Eliott feels about Daphne.'

'The way he feels has nothing to do with it,' returned Jane more heatedly than she intended. 'I don't think Daphne's any good for him—he'd be far better with someone else.'

Scott took hold of her arm and drew her away from the table, ignoring the protest that she had nothing on her plate.

'Just what is all this?' he demanded tersely. 'There seems to be something I don't know!'

'You ought not to have put temptation in Eliott's way!'

'Temptation?'

'Call it what you like. You had no right to leave the way clear for him.'

'Jane,' said Scott in a curt and commanding tone of voice, 'just why are you taking on this attitude to something that cannot possibly concern you in the least?'

She fell silent, biting her lip and wondering what explanation she could give. At last she said,

'I think that Eliott's far too nice for Daphne.'

Scott regarded her with a trace of perception but it was the frown knitting his brows which struck his companion most.

'Why the interest in Eliott's welfare?' he inquired in his slow Australian drawl. 'You only met him this evening.'

'I know, but that has nothing to do with the way I feel about him. As I've said, he's too nice for Daphne and I feel you've done him a great disservice in leaving the way clear for him to—well, court Daphne.'

Scott's eyes were narrowed as he said,

'You're not very flattering to Daphne, are you?'

She gave him a direct look.

'Neither have you been very flattering to Daphne. You humiliated her when you announced your engagement to me. You didn't care that you'd hurt her feelings, did you?'

He drew an impatient breath.

'I still don't know what this is all about. I feel I know some of it, but—'

'Some of it?' she broke in swiftly. 'What do you know?' Perhaps he suspected that Crystal liked Eliott and if he did then he'd done *her* a disservice too.

'I know that you are far more interested in Eliott than you ought to be. He's a stranger to you so you're just being silly, making all this fuss about his making up to Daphne. He happens to be in love with her and so—' Scott paused a moment for effect. 'And so, Jane, he's most unlikely to interest himself in any other girl.'

Jane looked down at her feet. So Scott did know that Crystal cared for Eliott. He also knew that it was no secret from her, Jane, either.

'I still think they're totally unsuited,' she said tautly. 'She'll play ducks and drakes with him.'

'That's your opinion,' he snapped and then, taking her arm, this time by no means gently, he propelled her towards the buffet table again.

* * *

It was over an hour later that Jane happened to see Eliott and Crystal together and appearing to be enjoying one another's company—if the smiles on their faces were anything to go by.

Daphne was nowhere in sight and neither was Scott. And as she turned to speak to Rachel who was standing with her, she saw Francis Woolcott approaching across the lawn.

'I wonder if I could speak to you privately?' he said, glancing apologetically at Rachel. 'I won't keep her a minute.'

'That's all right,' returned Rachel with a smile, and she went off before Jane had time to realise that she did not want to be left alone with Daphne's father.

'Yes?' she said rather coldly, wondering what the man could want with her.

'Can we sit down?' he suggested, glancing around and seeing that there were two chairs vacant at a small table under the trees. 'I must ask you something?' he said without preamble once they were seated. 'Are you and Scott really engaged to be married?'

Jane gave a start, her nerves going tight.

'Mr. Woolcott—what a th-thing to ask!' She endeavoured to appear shocked and indignant but feared she had not been very successful. His eyes were regarding her through half-closed lids.

'I myself have my doubts,' he told her frankly. 'It's just the kind of thing Scott would do if all else failed—'

'Please,' broke in Jane swiftly, 'don't say any more, Mr. Woolcott! Scott and I *are* engaged, and why you should doubt it I cannot think!' She was trying to be convincing and wishing with all her heart that someone would decide to come and join them before this man could say anything more. But of course no such prayed-for miracle came about and she was hearing Mr. Woolcott say,

'You and he haven't known one another long enough to have reached the stage where you could even think of marriage. And also, you're just a home help—'

'I'm Scott's private secretary,' she broke in to correct him.

'His secretary? Daphne said you were nothing more than a home help and that in consequence. . . .' He trailed off, catching his underlip between his teeth as he realised what he had said. He had been insulting but although Jane's temper was tested she did manage to hold it in check, merely asking what this was all about.

'You obviously have some very logical reason for seeking me out to speak of my engagement to Scott.'

'Both my wife and myself, having discussed what has happened, believe that the engagement is just a ruse to teach Daphne a lesson—that you have agreed to it, for a time, and that it will eventually be broken and then Scott will come back to my girl.' He sounded matter-of-fact, which seemed contradictory in that he was obviously troubled about what had occurred. Jane was reminded of her former opinion that, should his plans for his daughter fail to materialise, then he would accept it without complaint and take defeat gracefully. 'It doesn't ring true,' continued Francis Woolcott when Jane made no comment. 'You see, those of us who have known Scott for many years have learned that he'd never act without a great deal of prior thought—in any business deal, I mean. Yet, in the most serious matter of marriage he seems to have acted impulsively, and this being so totally out of character, there appears to be only one logical explanation—the one I have given you.' He sent her a sideways, challenging look and she was in no doubt at all that he knew he and his wife had hit on the truth.

Jane's nerves were tensed, her heart beating far too quickly, for she felt as if she had her back to the wall, with no choice presented to her but that of keeping quiet. Yet how long could she go without opening her mouth? She would have to say something. If she hotly maintained that the engagement was genuine then what were these people going to think when eventually it was broken? She would have to face them . . . or leave here. But if she left then what about Paddy? If only Paddy and Mary were married then she could go back home, but as things were Jane felt certain that Paddy would pursue her again.

'You're not saying anything. . . .' The voice was low and, to Jane's overwrought mind, insidious. 'Your silence is proof that there *is* something phoney about your engagement.'

'I shall let Scott speak to you,' she managed at last, a sudden fear assailing her because she was sure Scott would upbraid her for not managing to convince this man that the engagement was in fact genuine.

'Here is Scott now. I shall leave you to tell him what I have said—'

'No! Wait a moment!' But he was gone, leaving Jane seething and Scott standing above her with a frown of puzzlement on his face.

It did not take Jane long to relate what had transpired and just as she had thought, Scott began to reproach her for not trying to convince Francis that he was assuming something that was entirely false.

'Don't you blame me!' she flashed, forgetting she was nothing more than his employee and, therefore, ought to be treating him with the respect to which he was used. 'The engagement can't possibly appear genuine or Rachel and Crystal wouldn't have become suspicious! Everybody knows you so well, knows how you think and act—'

'How very clever of them,' cut in Scott icily. 'And how, may I ask, have you reached that conclusion?'

She felt the colour stain her cheeks as embarrassment washed over her at his arrogant attitude towards her. He was the Boss again, the man whom, she suspected, was ever conscious of his superiority over those to whom he gave employment.

'As a matter of fact,' she managed, 'Mr. Woolcott mentioned something of the kind. After all, people like you are bound to build up a reputation for certain behaviour in any given circumstance or situation, and so your action in becoming engaged to me—this when we hadn't even been keeping company, and when I was only your employee—naturally caused some amazement and speculation.'

His eyes were coldly arrogant as for a long moment he regarded Jane in silence.

'They can think what they like,' was his comment at last.

'But what about when the engagement's broken?' asked Jane and was instantly puzzled by the strange expression that settled on his face. He seemed to be scowling to himself!

'We'll not trouble ourselves about that unnecessarily,' he replied crisply. 'Bridges should be crossed when they are reached and not before.'

'There's talk going on,' she just had to remind him and without warning his eyes glinted and his mouth went tight.

'It's obvious that you want the engagement brought to an end!' he snapped. 'Well, you can forget it. For the time being the situation remains as it is, understand?'

She stared, bewildered by his manner for it was as if he suspected her of some secret reason for wanting the engagement to be terminated.

It was the very last thing she desired but unfortunately she was unable to divulge this without giving away her feelings for him.

Into the silence came laughter and both Scott and Jane turned their heads. Crystal was amused by something her companion was saying. Jane, turning to look at Scott, saw a flicker in his eyes as if he were faintly puzzled by the fact that Eliott was with Crystal when he could have been with Daphne.

He glanced around—looking for Daphne, decided

Jane, and saw the girl with her father and mother. She was watching the couple—Crystal and Eliott—an unfathomable expression on her face.

Scott said after a while,

'You do understand that the engagement continues?' and Jane was reminded that she hadn't commented on his previous words. She nodded her head.

'Yes, of course I understand,' she said, still puzzled by his manner.

'As long as you know,' he said tersely, and because his cousin was approaching he put his arm about her waist and smiled affectionately down at her.

When everyone had left it was well after midnight and both Crystal and her mother went straight to bed. But Jane was restless and sat on the verandah watching the moon and the stars and the cirrus clouds floating like veils of pure-spun silver as they stole the soft moonglow and impregnated themselves with it. She became aware of Scott and turned, surprised.

'I thought you had gone to bed,' she said, nerves fluttering because of the intimacy, the deep silence, the impression of being isolated from the rest of mankind. Over on the low hills and on the spinifex plains cattle were still, silhouetted in the silver effulgence of the light from the moon and stars.

'Aren't you tired?' he asked, ignoring her remark.

'I feel—restless.' She hadn't intended saying anything like that and hoped he would not pursue the matter, but she was disappointed to hear him say,

'Any particular reason?' His voice had a chill edge to it, she noticed.

'I suppose it's excitement. It was such a lovely evening, and it's still all new to me, remember. I expect the novelty will wear off eventually.'

He paused, his mouth tight.

'I saw you talking to Eliott just before he left.' The tone was devoid of expression but his face was hard. Again she was finding herself bewildered by his manner, which seemed to have something to do with Eliott—but what?

She murmured presently,

'Yes, he's really nice, isn't he?'

'A most sincere man.'

'How old is he?'

'Twenty-seven.'

'He looks a bit older.'

'Life in the Outback makes men look older.' Scott came close and looked into her upturned face. 'You're still very interested in Eliot,' he commented heartily. 'I've already warned you that no other woman stands a chance with him. He's in love with Daphne and has been for some considerable time.'

'Warned?' The one word seemed to register, burning into her mind. 'That's a strange word to use,' she said, staring at him in puzzlement.

The expression on his face gave nothing away.

'I'm just letting you know that there's no chance for any other woman,' he almost snapped.

'Yes, you've already said so.' She paused, still puzzled, and she was thinking of Crystal. 'I can't agree, though. If Daphne doesn't happen to return his affection—and I am very sure she doesn't—then he'll probably begin to forget her and fix his interest elsewhere.' It would be just the thing, she thought, if Eliot should fix his attention on Crystal. 'He'll have more sense than to pine forever over a girl whom he can't have.'

'You seem damned optimistic!' exploded Scott. 'Just you forget about his fixing his attention elsewhere, as you term it!'

Jane's eyes widened. She was more bewildered than ever by his manner.

'You really want him to marry Daphne, don't you?' she said, even though she had the strange impression that it was something else she should have been saying. 'You sound as if you've set your heart on it.'

Scott looked at her, his mouth compressed.

'Just why have you become so interested in him?' he demanded.

'I feel he's not suited to Daphne— Oh, I know that you said he was suited to her,' she went on swiftly when it seemed Scott would interrupt. 'It's a matter of opinion. . . .' Her voice trailed and her eyes became dreamy. She was a romantic and so obviously she was seeing Eliot and Crystal getting together. Her voice was almost tender as she went on, 'He deserves someone better,' and her eyes remained dreamy as she stared up into Scott's hard set face.

'I see. So whom do you consider is better?' he wanted to know, faintly jeering and scornful.

She frowned at him and said,

'You're in a very strange mood, Scott. Are you angry about something—about my saying these things about Eliot and Daphne?'

'You haven't answered my question,' he snapped.

136

Suddenly she felt her hackles rising.

'Nor have you answered mine!' she retaliated, chin in the air. 'What's wrong with you? You're like a bear with a sore head!'

Silence. The awful hush of anger and amazement.

'Jane,' he said in a dangerous soft voice, 'my employees do not speak to me like that.'

She coloured but it was mainly with anger.

But she just had to say,

'I happen to be your fiancée, too.' And to her surprise he nodded—in a grim, unfathomable kind of way—instead of reminding her that it was only a sham.

He surprised her still further by saying, deep emphasis in his tone,

'I'm glad you're remembering it.' His eyes were fixed and hard. 'Just you go on remembering it . . . or else!'

She stared in dumb amazement.

'This mood,' she began. 'Something's the matter—' She did not manage to get any further before her words were effectively silenced by the jerk she received as he brought her forward against his hard body. For a moment she felt the very breath had been knocked out of her. 'What—?'

'Just to remind you of your engagement to me— Oh, yes, you've a moment ago reminded *me* of it, but that doesn't mean I haven't to remind you!' And without further explanation of his extraordinary conduct he took possession of her lips, crushing them almost brutally just as he was crushing her body.

'Stop! What's the reason for this?' demanded Jane

when at last she was released and able to breathe. 'Are you crazy?'

'Very sane,' with a grim inflection that only served further to confuse her mind. 'So sane that I can see what you're after—what is going on in that mind of yours!'

'What I'm after?' Her brow furrowed and for a space she forgot the pain of her lips and of her body, although she did unconsciously endeavour to free herself from his punishing grip. 'Do you mind explaining?'

His eyes kindled.

'Don't come the innocent with me,' he rasped. 'I'm not in the mood for it! In fact, it's a very different mood I happen to be in—' He brought her to him again, and bent his head to lock his demanding mouth to hers. For a while she struggled, but it wasn't his force alone which brought about a cessation of her struggles. It was the awareness of his hands, roaming over her back, sliding downwards and causing quivers to flutter along her spine. Further thought of resistance dissolved altogether when she felt his hands within her bodice and vaguely she was angered that she was powerless to resist the pull of his male magnetism, to ignore the finesse with which he was playing with her breast, arrogantly enclosing it and as arrogantly possessing her lips at the same time. He was pressing against her soft curves in a deliberate attempt to force on her an awareness of his male hardness. She quivered as ecstasy tingled through her veins and she was vitally conscious of the pounding of her heart against him.

'Your skin's like silk. . . .' Scott's voice was throaty, low and vibrant. His lips against the alluring hollow of her throat were sensuous and moist. She felt his tongue begin to caress hers; sensed its intention to explore the sweet darkness of her mouth. Suddenly her whole frame was relaxed against his and her bones seemed almost to be turning to jelly. In her weakness she clung to him, her breathing ragged, all else forgotten in the urgency of her desire to be completely possessed. The pressure of his thigh was too strong for defence . . . even had she the desire to defend herself; her thighs parted and at the same time a tiny cry of protest came automatically to her lips, lips rosy and swollen from his love-making.

'Let's go inside . . . to your room. . . .' The words faded slowly as a gentle kiss replaced the final murmur, a kiss as soft and sweet as the touch of a summer breeze on a starlit night. All was magic; the sky was purple embroidered with silver, the mountains argent-painted by stolen moonglow. And the silence was total, primordial, like that great hush before the first life appeared on earth. Jane, lost in the paralysis of erotic languour, stood inert against the hard frame, her thighs still parted so that she was ever conscious of his need and, vaguely, that he would not let her go this time without that need being assuaged. All so intangible. . . . Heaven must be very close. . . .

It was an hour later when the floodgates opened for them both.

In her room Scott had undressed her, caressing her flesh all the time, moving slowly as if he savoured every new act and every new revelation that came before his passionate, admiring eyes. So tall above her! So masterful in all he was doing. When the bra was removed she instinctively put her hands down, lower, as if this last garment—so lacy and minute that it was scarcely any covering anyway—must remain, a guard to her modesty. She coloured deeply to hear him laugh, more deeply when his exploring hands slid down inside the dainty lace and for a long long moment they were immobile, just curled into the shape of her tender curves, while his lips moistly explored the exquisite lobes of her breasts, his tongue rough, teasing, feather-light—the prelude to the mastery of his teeth as they captured one erect nipple, imprisoning it while his tongue continued to tease and tempt. Little hushed exclamations escaped Jane as his passion increased, not gasps of protest, but tiny moans of rapture and sheer, undiluted bliss. Her one last garment went the way of the rest, and Scott lifted her and laid her on the bed. She watched him remove his jacket and his shirt, thrilling to the visual stimulation conveyed to her senses by the bronzed sheen of his chest and powerful shoulders, by the gleaming muscles of his arms. She turned away as he took off his slacks . . . and then he was beside her, his weight depressing the mattress, his naked body easing itself towards hers and at the contact of his whole length, at the sensuous awareness of his male need, desire and anticipation cascaded through and over her in fiery waves of erotic pleasure. Gladly she wound her arms about him, willingly accepted the long, unbelievable interlude of love-play which revealed his expertise and experience, and at the same time taught her so much she hadn't even imagined. Slowly, with the finesse of the artist, he brought her to that state whereby her enjoyment must be as great as his.

And when the vital moment was there her body melted in the volcanic heat of his passion and she surrendered to the triumph of his mastery over her. The heavens opened and fulfillment was complete; she floated into the realm of paradise, carried on the wings of ecstasy.

It was a long while later that he said, his body close, his limbs and hers entwined,

'And now, Jane, you know for sure that we're engaged to be married.'

Lost as she was in the torpor of after-play, Jane could not assemble her thoughts sufficiently to be able to assimilate anything but the actual words. Any subtler meaning totally escaped her. But because she knew he was waiting for her to speak, she obliged by saying languidly, and with an oncoming yawn,

'Yes, Scott, I now know for sure that we're engaged to be married.'

Chapter Nine

The following morning Scott's words rang in her ears the moment Jane awoke. He had left sometime in the early hours; she had been only vaguely aware of his almost silent departure. Now, as she lay stretched out, her eyes on the ceiling, she tried to puzzle out exactly what he had been getting at when those words were uttered. That there was some underlying meaning she now knew but what it was eluded her.

Or did it . . . ?

Had Scott's words been calculated to convey something other than the actual content?

Was it possible that the miracle had happened and that he wanted to marry her?

Jane's breath caught at the idea; she allowed her

mind to dwell on it for a space of two seconds and then dismissed such a notion as impossible. Scott had wanted her; she had known that she appealed to him physically. That was all. Nothing deeper was ever in his mind. He, the noble owner of Jacana Downs, an exalted member of the squatocracy. . . . How was it possible that he could fall in love with a mere home help! For that was what she had originally been, and still would have been had it not transpired that Scott happened to need a secretary, someone who could efficiently look after his accounts.

It was strange, she was telling herself as she dressed after taking her bath, that she had no feeling of embarrassment. It was the first 'adventure' of that kind, the first time a man had ever come anywhere near to intimacy with her . . . and yet here she was, unashamed, unembarrassed. She recalled the last time, when Scott had almost had his way with her—she had been embarrassed then, hating to face him the next day, declaring she would leave his employment.

He was in the breakfast room when she entered, and she did colour a little then, because of the strange enigmatic smile that came to his fine lips and hovered there. His dark eyes slid over her and she wondered if he were stripping her.

He said suavely, flicking a hand towards a chair,

'Sit down, Jane,' but then he went over and drew the chair out for her.

She said quietly,

'Thank you, Scott,' and looked down at her hands. He gave a light laugh, tilted her chin, then kissed her gently on the mouth.

'There is a lot to do today.' His voice became brisk as he began to outline the work he had for her to do. 'Letters are a headache to me and so I want you to learn to answer most of them yourself and merely bring them to me for signing.'

There were also books to be brought up to date, and some bills to be paid.

'You can make out the cheques,' he told her casually. 'I'll let you have my cheque book.'

Jane's eyes widened.

'You'd give me your cheque book?' she gasped.

A frown tinged his brow.

'Why not?'

'Well. . . .' She became at a loss for words. 'I meant—it isn't usual for a boss to trust an employee with his cheque book. . . .' She broke off at his expression, and shivered slightly in her bewilderment.

'But you are not merely an employee, are you?' murmured Scott in a very soft tone of voice. 'We established the real relationship last night, remember?'

'Scott,' she faltered, 'I don't understand.' She looked at him across the table, her eyes wide, imploring as she went on, 'Our engagement . . . it wasn't supposed to be anything other than a sham. I've always regarded myself as—'

'Free?' The words came forth with the sharpness of the crack of a whip and she jumped in her chair. 'You're not free! Understand? Not free, so you can just resign yourself to the fact that you're irrevocably tied to me.'

Jane stared, her throat dry, her mind more confused than ever before.

'Are—are you saying that—that you w-want to marry me?' It was out at last, and as soon as the words were spoken she regretted them, but for what specific reason she could not have explained.

'I want to marry you,' was the quietly spoken response to her question. 'We shall discuss the date later—perhaps this evening.'

'I still don't understand,' she complained, in a voice which could only be described as fractious. The thing was—she wanted to know why he was willing—no, *eager*—to marry her. Obviously he wasn't in love with her or he would have said so, she concluded quite logically. 'You must have a reason for wanting to marry me.'

'I do have a reason.' Suddenly he was lifting a hand to smother a yawn, and just as suddenly Jane felt a stab of anger that was almost a physical sensation, so strong was its effect on her. So cool, he was, sitting there waiting for his breakfast to come! So calm about wanting to marry her! And he had never even proposed! He had simply stated that he wanted to marry her and as far as her feelings were concerned he just wasn't interested! Talk about the feudal system of ancient times in England—this wasn't in it!

That nothing would have made her happier than to become his wife could not be denied, but he did not want to marry her for love. It was with remarkable control that she was able to say, in quietly modulated tones,

'And that reason, Scott?'

He seemed to pause in thought and, watching him intently, Jane felt sure that some kind of a confession lingered on his tongue. But if so he did not utter it.

'It needn't trouble you—'

'Not trouble me!' she cut in wrathfully, unable to hold her temper in check any longer. 'You *tell* me I'm to marry you! Tell me!' she repeated, shouting the words and bringing angry colour to his face. It rose at both sides of his mouth in threads of crimson that spread to brighten his cheeks. But Jane was not deterred; she was far too angry herself for that. 'You haven't even asked me if I want to marry you,' she went on to remind him. And then she added, driven on by some force she was totally unable to control, 'For your information, Scott, I wouldn't marry you if you were the last man on earth!'

Not at all original—trite in fact and she blushed a little. As for the man opposite to her—his face was a glowering mask and his hand resting on the tablecloth was clenched.

'So,' he said contemptuously at last, 'you're not averse to sleeping with a man you have no intention of marrying?'

Jane gave a start, and was conscious of having forgotten all about last night! Anger, and the knowledge that although he did not love her Scott was ready to marry her, had overshadowed completely the drama and beauty of last night.

She found no immediate reply for she was now embarrassed and humiliated by his manner, but his accusation that meant, in effect, that she would sleep with any man who took her fancy. Her thoughts very naturally swung to Margaret, and the respect she had received here at Jacana Downs, received not only from Scott, but from all the other men as well. And this was solely owning to her keeping her self-respect by refusing to be tempted into an affair. A sport, Scott had called her, Jane, while Margaret was not a sport.

And at the end of the day it was girls like Margaret whom men serious for marriage preferred.

All this brought Jane back to the question: why did Scott want to marry her when obviously he believed her to be cheap?

She looked at him and thought of questioning him, but then remembered that she had just said quite categorically that she would not marry him, and so there really wasn't an excuse for questioning him.

'I've just spoken to you,' he reminded her almost harshly. 'Aren't you going to comment?'

'Of course.' Jane's voice was low, husky with emotion. 'It isn't true that I'd sleep with a man I have no intention of marrying.'

Scott's eyebrows lifted a fraction.

'But you've just refused to marry me,' he said.

Soft colour rose to tint Jane's pale cheeks.

'You know what I mean,' she parried, relieved to see Anna enter with a large silver tray which she set down on the sideboard.

'Shall I serve it out, Boss?' she asked. 'Or would you rather do it yourself?'

'You can leave it there,' he said shortly. 'But bring over the coffee pot.'

This she did, then poured the coffee. When the door had closed behind her Scott said tersely,

'I'm afraid I don't know what you mean. You've slept with me and yet you refuse to marry me.' His eyes swept her over with undisguised contempt. 'What am I supposed to think?'

She paused a moment, watching him closely. That contempt was still in his eyes . . . and yet she had the strange conviction that he was *not* in fact reflecting his innermost thoughts.

'I feel,' she said a trifle wearily at length, 'that we are both wasting our time in talking. I don't want to discuss the matter any more.' She changed the subject abruptly after taking a few sips of her coffee. 'This work you say is urgent—I'd better get on with my breakfast so that I can start.'

Scott's eyes kindled, but to her relief he allowed the subject to drop and instead kept to the purely business matter of the work he wanted Jane to get through that day.

The brumbie was standing motionless on the hill while Jane, thrilling to his sheer wild and male beauty, stood just as motionless, watching him. His head was high, mane moving in the breeze. His body shone with health . . . but when eventually he moved Jane was horrified to see him limping painfully.

'Oh. . . .' Her soft heart went out to him; she pondered for a moment, wondering what could be done. If she told Scott, or any of the other men, the brumbie would undoubtedly be captured and en- slaved to the whims of those who wanted to ride him.

Yes, captured and *held* captive, not brought in and treated for his injury, then given his freedom again. The horse could not move very quickly at all, and it was obvious that he was in great pain. He urgently needed a vet.

Jane's decision tore her apart, for the only alternatives were either to let him go on in pain, and perhaps die from whatever injury he had sustained, or have him brought into the paddock where, once cured, he would be broken, and then harnessed.

For fully five minutes she watched the agonisingly slow progress of the beautiful creature, and she thought of his pride in his freedom. Perhaps he had a mate, and a foal. Tears came to Jane's eyes and her throat seemed tight and swollen. She felt foolish but the tears persisted and she was knuckling her eyes when to her disgust and dismay she became conscious of another presence on the verandah. She thought: I ought to have known someone would be here soon, seeing that it's getting on for four o'clock, and tea will soon be served.

'What's the matter?' Scott's voice held concern but no real anxiety. 'Why the tears?'

She gulped and searched for a handkerchief. With a sigh that might have been born of impatience Scott gave her his handkerchief and said shortly,

'Don't you ever carry one of these? Perhaps I ought to buy you a dozen next time I go into town.'

'Sarcasm's not for moments like this,' she snapped. 'I'm trying to make a decision!'

'You are?' grittingly. 'Well, I can make an intelligent guess at what it is.'

'You can?' She blinked as she held out the handker-chief for him to take back. 'So you've seen him, too.'

'Him?' with a sudden frown. 'Who?' Automatically Scott glanced around. 'What are you talking about?'

'The—' Something made her stop. 'This intelligent guess,' she frowned, 'what is it?'

Scott seemed almost to glower at her and she had the impression that he believed her to be prevaricating about something, putting on an act of innocence that was calculated to deceive him. He said slowly and tautly,

'You said you were trying to make a decision. What it was obviously caused you much heartache.'

She nodded, bewildered.

'Yes, it did.'

'So much so that you cried over it.'

'Yes.' She paused, surreptitiously looking for the brumbie. She was sure now of course that Scott was unaware of its presence there, on the rise. 'This intelligent guess,' she said again. 'You baffle me, Scott—oh, in so many ways! Why are you so cryptic—'

'It's you who are obtuse! No,' he corrected coldly, 'you merely assume the pose! But I'm not fooled.'

She drew an exasperated breath but said nothing. The plight of the brumbie was the most pressing thing on her mind at the moment. She loved all animals but horses and dogs especially. Where had the brumbie gone to? It couldn't have gone far— There it was, by a clump of grasses—lying down! She watched Scott but his attention was all with her at the moment. She would thrash it all out with him later, she decided once and for all. This evasion was getting on her nerves. He could just come out with whatever was bothering him! But for now. . . . Again she was asking herself what was best for the horse. And when it suddenly occurred to her that it was becoming so helpless that it could not possibly survive for long, she found her decision to be easy, albeit reluctantly reached.

'Scott,' she murmured, her eyes flickering to the horse again, 'that brumbie, remember—the one you said you wished you could catch and tame?'

'Well?' He was frowning impatiently. 'What the devil's the brumbie to do with anything?'

'It's lame.'

'Lame? How do you know?' Expressionless the tone but in his face eager anticipation. 'Have you seen it recently?'

She pointed, her action as hesitant as her decision had been.

'It's over there—I think you can see it if you follow accurately the way I'm pointing.'

'By heaven, yes!' All else was forgotten. 'He's lame, you say?'

Again she nodded her head.

'He was standing a short while ago, then he began to move and I saw that he was lame—and I believe he's in great pain. What do you think has happened to him?' The distress in her voice obviously fell on deaf ears for all Scott said was,

'I don't know, but I'm soon going to find out! What a beauty! And he'll be mine!'

'He ought to be mine,' she said but Scott did not

hear. He was away, running towards the saddling paddock, shouting an order as he went. Jane saw the roustabout lift his head to listen, then a few moments later Scott was racing over the spinifex plain, a lassoo in his hand.

'What's going on?' Crystal's voice at her side brought Jane's attention from the rider on which her eyes had been fixed, admiring eyes despite the fact of her hating his errand.

She explained about the brumbie, heard Crystal give a low whistle before saying,

'Scott'll be thrilled if he catches it. He's wanted that brumbie for over two years to my knowledge. He and others have made many attempts to capture him but always he's been too swift, or clever, for them. But now it looks as if Scott's to get his wish—and won't many others be jealous!'

'He'll be caught only because he's lame. It'll be unsportsmanlike if Scott keeps him in captivity after he's better of whatever ails him.' The emotion in Jane's voice caused it to shake a little and Crystal stared at her.

'You don't like the idea of his being broken?' she asked.

'No, I do not!'

'Scott will be very kind to it, believe me.'

Jane knew that already, but the knowledge couldn't dispel the ache within her at the thought of that proud, free horse becoming subservient to a master.

'He ought to have it cured then let it go,' she quivered. 'It's unfair if he keeps it.'

Crystal looked curiously at her.

'You're his fiancée,' she said slowly, 'so he ought by rights to do you a favour.'

The inflection in the girl's voice could not possibly be misinterpreted.

'You still believe we're not really engaged, don't you?'

'I'm not the only one, Jane.'

'Others . . . ? They're all talking about me?'

'You both. They're wondering why it's happening.'

'Waiting for it to end?'

Crystal hesitated a moment and then, as if the words were being spoken to someone incalculable,

'I strongly suspect that you find it embarrassing to be tackled like this on the subject.' Crystal was plainly interested in her reply but Jane's temper was rising and all she said was,

'Shall we revert to the original subject, Crystal?'

'The brumbie?' Crystal gave a swift, self-depre-cating shrug of her shoulders. 'I've been snubbed and I suppose I asked for it. All the same, many people are exceedingly puzzled by a situation that seems artificial, to say the least—'

'Please, Crystal!' broke in Jane in anger. 'Forget your suspicions! If you must ask questions about our engagement, then go to Scott!' and without affording the girl any opportunity of speaking Jane turned and left her standing there, the most thoughtful expression on her face.

It was the following morning and Jane was standing by the paddock rail watching the brumbie cropping grass when she heard her name spoken.

'Elliot!' A swift smile took the brooding expression from her face. 'What are you doing here?'

'I've come to see Crystal. Is she about?'

'Crystal. . . .' Jane's eyes lit with pleasure. 'Yes, she's just had a swim and gone to change. She'll be joining me here in a few minutes.'

'Why here?' He looked nonplussed until Jane turned to point in the direction of where the brumbie was, by the far fence, his front leg in a splint. Elliot's jaw dropped. 'The brumbie!' he gasped. '*The* one! But how—? What's wrong with its leg?'

'Broken,' answered Jane briefly but then went on to explain.

'So Scott's the lucky one.' He looked almost sulky and there was no mistaking the envious note in his voice. 'That brumbie's been on my territory for weeks. I'd become used to the idea that eventually he'd be mine.'

Jane said evenly,

'He happens to be mine, Elliot, and once he's well again he'll be set free.' She turned to face him, ignored the stunned expression as she continued, 'If he is set free, I hope that you, and everyone else who in the past has been interested in him, will respect my wishes that he remain free.' She did not know quite how she managed the courage for this, but she did know that she was striving for the impossible. The brumbie at close quarters was even more beautiful than when seen at a distance, and if by some miracle Scott could be persuaded to set him free, he would still be desired by others.

'You say he's yours?' Elliot looked at her with a puzzled expression. 'How can that be? I expect it was Scott who captured him?'

'It was, but only because I happened to see the horse and realised it was lame. It transpired that it had somehow become caught in fencing and on breaking free it broke its leg. It had other injuries besides the broken leg—injuries sustained while it was trying to free itself.' Her voice caught because of the strength of emotion within her. 'Scott would never ever have captured him if he hadn't been lame, and so he must let him go!'

Elliot looked at her with perception.

'You're not at all sure that Scott will regard the brumbie as yours,' he said and with a sigh and a nod she agreed. 'But as his fiancée you can surely persuade him to do as you wish?'

She paused a moment and then said,

'Have you heard any rumours, Elliot?'

His good-natured face became wooden.

'Regarding what, Jane?'

She swallowed, searching for words and wishing she had not broached the subject. At last she said, looking straightly at him,

'There have been suspicions that our engagement isn't real.' There, it was out and she would now discover just what was being said among the other ranchers.

'As you know, Scott was very friendly with Daphne.'

She nodded her head, marvelling at this conversation, the intimacy and the complete lack of restraint between her and this charming young man whom she hoped would become interested in Crystal.

She said,

'Would you like some coffee, Elliot? Crystal takes ages to get herself ready. We'll be on our own because Rachel's over at the hairdresser's.'

'You want to talk to me?' he said perceptively.

'I feel I can do so without your passing it on,' was all Jane replied to that.

They went on to the verandah and soon Anna was there with the coffee tray. Jane poured, handed Elliot his coffee and said,

'You must have heard the rumours, Elliot.'

'Yes,' he owned, 'I have. Daphne's father, though resigned in a way, actually told someone that your engagement was merely a sham and that Scott was hoping to bring Daphne to her senses.'

'I see. . . .' She coloured, as was to be expected. 'And everyone else?'

He shrugged casually.

'The situation lends itself to gossip, you must agree?'

'Of course.' Leaning forward, she picked up her cup and saucer. 'Do you believe the engagement to be a sham?' Even as she asked the question Jane was thinking of Scott and wondering what he would have to say should he ever know about this conversation. He'd be furious . . . and that, she decided grimly, was putting it mildly indeed! Thoughts naturally progressed and she was again dwelling on his attitude in regards to the engagement. For despite her firm assertion that she would not marry him he still put on the act of being affectionate to her whenever his cousin or her daughter were about.

'I would rather not give you my opinion of the business,' returned Elliot after a long pause.

'You,' she murmured then left in abeyance what she was going to say. 'As we're talking so—well—intimately, then I suppose I can ask what your feelings are for Daphne?'

'I ought to be surprised by that question,' he smiled, 'but I'm not because I guess Scott's told you that I'm in—' He stopped so abruptly that Jane was startled. His mouth had gone tight and for a fleeting moment he looked actually aggressive. "I *used* to have a crush on the girl,' he finished and the utterance of that confession seemed to dissolve his anger. 'You were about to say something?' he added before Jane could speak.

'I was going to comment on the fact that you've come over today to see Crystal.' A question as to his reason but she hadn't quite been able to phrase it as one. It seemed far too pertinent a query.

Elliot sipped his steaming coffee and for a long moment there was silence between them.

And neither was aware of being watched by a pair of dark eyes that smouldered. . . .

It was Jane who eventually broke the silence.

'You're obviously no longer interested in Daphne, then?'

He said candidly,

'I still feel something for her, Jane . . . she's so lovely. . . .' His face softened to tenderness and for some reason of his own he put forth a hand to cover Jane's as it rested on the rattan table at which they were both sitting, opposite to one another. Vines above provided shade and a bougainvillaea entwined itself around slender pillars as if to add beauty and a romantic atmosphere to the scene. Jane smiled at the action, her thoughts soaring to the possibility of a match between Elliot and Crystal. She waited, though, for Elliot to finish what he had been about to say. 'But beneath the veneer, Jane—' He looked at her for a long moment. 'What is beneath it? Scott obviously changed his mind about her and so have I changed my mind.' He paused and she felt his fingers tighten on her hand. 'I want permanence based on love and respect when I marry, and I know I would never have that with Daphne. With someone different, someone like—' He stopped abruptly and on noting his expression Jane swung around in her chair.

'Scott!' She smiled at him and then was amazed at the response. Never had she seen him quite so gloweringly formidable as he was at this moment. 'What's wrong?' she quavered. 'The brumbie. . . .' But it couldn't be anything to do with the brumbie that had made Scott as furiously angry as this!

'Elliot,' stiffly as Scott's eyes seemed to bore into the hand that was covering that of his fiancée. Swiftly it was withdrawn and a self-conscious tint of colour crept into Elliot's cheeks. 'Why are you here?'

Jane frowned at the tone, while Elliot seemed only puzzled.

'I—er—came to see Crystal. . . .' Even to Jane's ears that sounded lame and she did wonder what was wrong with Elliot. It must be that he was feeling embarrassed at being discovered to be interested in Crystal when, as far as Scott was concerned, he ought to have had eyes only for Daphne.

'Where is she?' Scott's eyes moved to Jane; his tone was distinctly skeptical. 'Crystal, eh?'

Jane's frown deepened. What on earth was the matter with Scott these days! He was acting almost irrationally!

'She's in her room, changing,' she vouchsafed shortly, and she turned away and picked up her coffee cup.

The atmosphere could have been cut with a knife! Jane, bewildered and angry with Scott for his inexplicable behaviour, rose from her chair and said with a scowl for Scott and a smile for his friend, 'I'll go and get her.'

She had not expected Scott to follow her into the house but he did. She swung around to face him.

'What *is* the matter with you?' she demanded belligerently. 'What do you want?'

The dark eyes kindled dangerously.

'Be very careful,' he warned with a harsh inflection. He let his eyes slide over her from head to foot. 'Crystal!' he scoffed. 'Do you two suppose I'm that much of a fool?'

'You—!' Jane stood motionless, blinking at him while her bewildered brain tried vainly to comprehend. 'What exactly are you getting at?'

Scott's mouth compressed, but before he could speak Crystal appeared, looking chic and lovely in a white cotton dress trimmed with pale green piping round the collar and the belt. Her hair shone; her lips were rosy and full. She paused in her stride across the room and seemed puzzled.

'Something wrong?' she wanted to know.

'Elliot's come to see you,' began Jane but she was rudely interrupted by Scott's saying roughly,

'I'll see *you* later. In any case, you ought to be in the office—working!'

'I was merely looking at the brumbie for a few minutes—' Jane broke off, flushing painfully as Scott swung on his heel and left the room.

'Well, what do you know about that?' from Crystal who had turned to stare at his broad back. 'What's caused him to do his nut like that?'

Jane looked at her.

'I have the most absurd and unbelievable notion,' she murmured with a faraway look in her eyes, 'that —that Scott is—is jealous. . . .'

'Jealous?' blinked Crystal. 'Of whom?'

Jane's eyes drifted to the figure of the man sitting on the verandah.

'Elliot's come to see you,' she repeated. 'Don't keep him waiting any longer, Crystal.'

'But—what the hell's going on?'

'I wish I knew,' returned Jane with a sigh. 'If only I could be sure?'

'Oh, for pity's sake cut out these obscure remarks! What the devil should Scott be jealous about?'

'Elliot was—was holding my—' Jane pulled herself up with a jerk. 'You'd best go and see what he wants,' she advised and made her escape before Crystal in her exasperation could question her further.

Chapter Ten

It was less than half an hour before Scott was standing over his fiancée as she sat at the typewriter in her office. He had stormed in, banging the door after him, and now he tossed his slouch hat onto a sofa and was glowering down at her. She had been thinking fast for the last half-hour and had come to the conclusion that Scott was either adopting a dog-in-the-manger attitude or he really was jealous of Elliot. In which case. . . .

The idea of his having fallen in love with her was too heady and as on a previous occasion she turned it aside, trying to convince herself that the former idea was the correct one.

'Well,' he began raspingly, 'what have you to say for yourself?'

'What do you mean, Scott? You've been acting most strangely—'

'Cut it out!' he almost snarled and before she could even guess at his intention she was roughly jerked to her feet, brought to his hard body, her chin tilted with a hard hand beneath it and then she was subjected to a bruising kiss so prolonged and sensuous that she felt her breath caught in her throat and had the sensation of choking. Desperately she began to struggle, and when at last he decided to release her she felt weak and drained, gulping in air while fury consumed her. She took support from the back of her chair, glared at him, did no more than snatch off her engagement ring, throw it at him and tell him to go to hell.

Such an outburst was plainly unexpected, and if it hadn't been for the fact of her anger Jane could have laughed at the expression of amazement on Scott's face.

He seemed actually to gape at her, undoubtedly taken aback and some imp of mischief she could not control urged Jane to say, before he could speak,

'You've never been spoken to like that before, I suppose! Well, Scott, there's a first time for everything and I've taken about as much from you as I can stand. How dare you come in here and grab me like that? No doubt some of your women in the past have enjoyed the he-man tactics but for myself—I don't intend to collect bruises, so just you remember that in future—not that there is any future!' she thought to add, just for the satisfaction of goading him. She watched the crimson threads of sheer fury creep along the sides of his mouth and automatically took a strategic step backwards. But Scott was between her and the door and she realised she wasn't doing any good merely by putting another yard or so between them. 'I'm leaving here,' she added swiftly, 'so you can arrange transport for me!'

He looked at her long and hard for fully thirty seconds, and then, pointing to the ring which, having hit the wall, had bounced back and was now on the carpet by the desk, he said slowly,

'Pick it up, Jane.'

'Why? Is it your intention to force it back onto my finger?' Her eyes travelled arrogantly over him. 'I'll not deny that it's possible, but how do you propose to keep it there?'

'You made a bargain with me.' His voice, though vibrating with anger, was quiet, and the drawl rather more pronounced. 'Pick that ring up,' he ordered again, adding that if she didn't obey him he would make her, and he thought to remind her of the occasion when he had compelled her to stoop and pick up his handkerchief. She hesitated, but the expression on his face only convinced her that she would be imprudent to defy him, would assuredly bring upon herself the sort of humiliation she would not soon forget. But it was with slow, reluctant steps that she moved and bent down. She felt hot as she placed the ring on the desk without looking at him, for she was sure he would be regarding her with a sneering, mocking expression in his eyes. Arrogant wretch!

'Give me your hand,' he ordered and with a deep

sigh of resignation she obeyed again. 'And now,' he said when it was back on her finger, 'you can explain just why you were allowing Elliot to hold your hand out there, where anyone passing could see!'

She stared, wishing fervently that anger was not controlling her mind to the exclusion of all else. Her lips were hurting and so was her body—she felt he had intended to crush her ribs to pulp. And the result was that anger, overwhelming and uncontrollable, was all that filled her being. She felt at this moment that she hated him . . . and yet her subconscious reminded her that she loved him.

After a few seconds a modicum of commonsense made her say,

'Neither of us is in a fit state of mind to discuss anything, and so please let us talk later, when we've both calmed down.'

He was shaking his head. The consequence was that Jane's anger rose swiftly again.

'When did this affair begin?' he demanded harshly. 'When, I said! Answer me!'

'I. . . .' To her consternation and disgust Jane started to cry. 'Leave me alone!' she almost shouted at him. 'Go away and mind your own business! If I want Elliot to hold my hand then what has it to do with you? I enjoyed it; he enjoyed it— Oh, let go of me!'

But Scott's fury, greater even than hers, spurred him to an action he knew he would regret. He shook Jane unmercifully, shook her till he himself was breathless, and then he had to hold on to her arms, supporting her for she would have collapsed from sheer weakness if he had let her go. The tears flooded her cheeks; sobs racked her body. She felt physically ill, and looked up into his face through eyes almost blinded with tears.

'I hate you,' she sobbed, 'hate you. Get that!'

'I don't doubt it,' he gritted. 'But all the same, you are engaged to me and it stays that way!' He sat her down on the chair and moved towards the door. 'Get yourself a wedding dress ordered,' he said roughly. 'We'll be married within a week!' And on that he was gone, the door closing with surprising quietness behind him.

Two days went by and Jane did not see Scott. He had gone to Sydney and had merely left a note on Jane's desk to say he would be away on business until the weekend. She felt lost, and more depressed than ever in her life before. With all anger evaporated she was able to see a clear picture, and it made her miserable that Scott was not here so that everything could be cleared up between them. Both had said hurtful things to one another, untrue things born of pride and the reluctance of either to back down and be the first to say, 'I love you.' Yes, it was simple as that, yet they had quarrelled fiercely, and Scott had hurt her. But she had forgiven him, knowing he was sorry, and all she wanted was to relax in his arms and tell him all that was in her heart.

Rachel came to her as she sat after taking her morning coffee from the office to the verandah.

'Perhaps,' began Rachel in a tone of impatience, 'you'll tell me what the devil's going on around here? First there's your engagement which obviously was entered into to make Daphne pull up her socks! Then Elliot takes over and plays up to the wretched girl, who plainly doesn't want him anyway! And now—he's been on the doorstep for the past three days and today he and Crystal have gone off to town—what for, might I ask?'

Jane said she had no idea, but secretly she hoped it might be for an engagement ring . . . or perhaps it was early days for that just yet. Nevertheless, it was clear that, very soon, an engagement between the two would be announced. How Crystal had managed to remain so cool about it all Jane did not know, since she was sure that the girl was blissfully happy at the unexpected turn of events. Elliot had confided to Jane that although he had believed himself to be in love with Daphne, he had always had a soft spot for Crystal.

'I used always to be sort of—excited whenever Scott said she and her mother were coming for a visit,' he confessed. 'It now seems very strange that I didn't examine my feelings for Crystal more deeply.'

'Daphne's so appealing, outwardly,' Jane reminded him. 'And of course it does add to the attraction when the one you want is pretty well hooked with someone else.'

Elliot had agreed.

'But it was never what I feel for Crystal,' he owned. And he had added slowly, 'I hope she won't ever hold it against me that I might have hurt her by appearing to be mad about Daphne?'

'Not her. Crystal's very happy, Elliot, and so what is past can't ever be important to her.'

To Jane's relief Elliot had not mentioned the little scene enacted when Scott had come upon them on the verandah, when Elliot was holding her hand. In his absorption with Crystal he had obviously forgotten all about it.

'I've asked you a question, Jane!' Rachel's sharp voice severed Jane's musings and she looked up.

'About Crystal and Elliot? It should be plain to you—as it is to me—that they're falling in love with each other.'

Rachel's eyes flickered.

'I hadn't dared to hope,' she admitted.

'Well, it's plain enough now,' repeated Jane. 'You're happy about it, then?'

'You sound doubtful.'

'It means you'll be on your own.'

'I never did want Crystal to be tied to my apron strings. Yes, I'm happy about the situation.' A small pause and then, with a curious inflection,

'You didn't comment on my remark about your own affair with Scott.'

'You and Crystal doubt the engagement—you think it's a sham?'

Rachel smiled but somehow it meant nothing; she was smiling to herself, that was all.

'You yourselves know best whether it's a sham or not,' was all she had to say about that, and she would have changed the subject but Jane persisted,

'You never did have any real faith in the engagement, did you, Rachel?'

'It was so obvious.'

'The reason for it, you mean?'

'Exactly.' Rachel's tone was dry.

'You believe that Scott is still enamoured with Daphne?'

'He has so much to gain by marrying her.'

'Materially, yes, I agree,' Jane was swift to accede, but she went on to add that money wasn't everything in life. 'It doesn't always make a contribution to happiness,' she said finally.

'Does a man like Scott bother his head about anything more than increasing his wealth? They're all the same, these rich graziers; they want more and more, and marrying the heiress to an estate like the one owned by Daphne's father is an easier way than most of acquiring great wealth.'

Jane wanted to laugh, knowing as she did that Rachel was in for a surprise. She could not help wondering what her reaction would be were she to tell her that Scott had ordered her to see about a wedding dress as they were to be married within a week.

A week. . . . Just like Scott to say a thing like that, in his domineering way. He knew full well it couldn't be done.

'Have you spoken of these suspicions to Scott himself?' she inquired at length and Rachel shook her head.

'I don't deliberately leave myself open for one of Scott's biting set-downs,' she answered with a grim edge to her voice. 'He'd probably tell me to go to the devil!'

Jane did laugh then, but changed the subject, asking Rachel what she thought about the brumbie.

'According to Kelly, one of the stockmen, he's

doing fine—mainly because he's generally in excellent shape. He was doing his best to get out this morning, by the way.'

'He's always showing us all that he resents being cooped up in that paddock.'

'They put him in the breaking paddock. I expect his days of freedom are over.'

'Not if I have my way!'

'Scott'll not part with him. Crystal told me how you feel, and that you consider the horse to be yours. But it was Scott who brought him in and it'll be Scott who'll make the final decision. Make no mistake about that,' she went on to warn Jane. 'He's wanted that brumbie far too long to let it go, mark my words. Besides, he knows that if the horse were loose then all the others would be trying again to catch him. Scott would be as mad as hell if he let him go to please you and then someone else captured and broke him.'

Jane bit her lip in vexation. How could she stake her claim to ownership of the brumbie? If that were possible then she could let it go free and it would be protected, simply because everyone would know that it had an owner already. She was thoughtful for a long while after Rachel had left her. And by the time she returned to her office there was a very determined expression on her face.

Chapter Eleven

It was very late in the evening when Scott returned. Jane had been sitting with Rachel and Crystal, enjoying the cool of the evening while drinking after-dinner liqueurs and coffee. She had been restless all day, as Scott had let her know over the air that he would be back. She began to worry about the plane, wondering if anything had gone wrong. She half-feared that Scott was stranded somewhere in the desert. Or even had a more serious mishap.

'I should go to bed,' Rachel had advised, eyeing Jane perceptively. She had during the past couple of days deduced that whatever the reason for the engagement, Jane was madly in love with her fiancé.

'Staying up won't bring him back any quicker. Take it from me, Scott's okay with an airplane. He'll not have crashed.'

Crystal had added her assurances and then both she and her mother had gone to bed, but Jane, restless and also with much more on her mind to add to its confusion, knew it would be futile to go to bed. She would not sleep a wink.

Her heart jerked when at last she heard the sound she was so intently listening for. The plane coming down, and a few minutes later the engine of the ute as it came to the forecourt of the homestead. Voices; one of the rouseabouts had stayed up so he could take the ute out to the airstrip once he heard the plane coming in. All so loyal and thoughtful for the Boss!

Scott took the steps of the verandah with the lithe spring of an athlete for he had noticed Jane, who had risen to her feet and was standing by the rail, her slender form silhouetted against the dim amber background of soft lights both from the wall lights of the room behind and from the glow of the lamps hidden in the trellised vines. Her hair was tousled and she brushed a hand through it—but she scarcely cared what she looked like, so great was her relief at seeing Scott safe and sound.

And, she fervently hoped, in a better frame of mind than when he had left her!

'What's wrong?' he wanted to know, glancing at his wrist watch. 'It's gone one o'clock.'

'I waited for you.' She was unsure of herself all at once. 'I felt worried.'

'About me?' Was there a cynical edge to his soft Australian drawl, or did she imagine it?

'Did you have a good trip?' Silly, inane question. She could find nothing else to say.

'I did all I went for,' he answered briefly. He stood staring down at her for a long moment and then, 'Were you really worried?' he asked and she nodded her head, feeling tears collecting in a cloud behind her eyes. She had expected him to be more kindly disposed to her than this, for after all he, too, had had time to ponder and to realise that the quarrel hadn't really been necessary— She halted her thoughts as it suddenly occurred to her that he was probably still half-convinced that it was Elliot she cared for.

'Can I make you some coffee?' she managed, forced to break the oppressive silence. 'I—I could do with some myself, as—as a matter of fact.'

Rising as she spoke she came closer to him than intended. He caught her wrist, brought her to him and kissed her almost roughly on the lips.

Be careful, she whispered to herself, or you'll be crying buckets!

'Did you get someone to make that dress?' Scott held her from him but kept her prisoner by the grip on her arms. She shook her head.

'There isn't anyone. I'd have to go to town—I expect.'

Scott's eyes flickered.

'So you are going to marry me, then?'

She said quietly, not looking at him,

'You made it clear that I had to.'

'I know, and you know, that I couldn't force you to marry me.'

Her eyes registered surprise.

'I'd not have expected an admission like that from you,' she said.

'Go and make the coffee. We've a lot to talk about—'

'Scott,' she broke in.

'Yes?'

'Elliot and Crystal are getting married. I'll—'

'What!'

'I'll leave you to take that in while I make the coffee,' she said over her shoulder as she made her way towards the open French window leading from the verandah to the living-room. 'I hope its significance strikes you,' she added with a hint of sarcasm. She hadn't been able to resist that parting shot.

'Jane! Come back—' But she was gone, leaving a very puzzled Scott behind her. He was sitting in one of the chairs when she returned with the tray and set it down on the table.

'When did this happen?' he wanted to know.

'Elliot has liked her for some time, but he believed it was Daphne he loved.' She had poured the coffee and she pushed his towards him. 'Rachel's delighted.'

'And you?' he challenged in an expressionless voice. 'Are you delighted?'

'I'm thrilled. I did tell you that in my opinion Elliot deserved someone better than Daphne, if you remember?'

His mouth set.

'I remember,' was his grim rejoinder. 'You let me believe—'

'I didn't let you believe anything, Scott. You took it for granted that I was thinking of myself as a likely candidate for Elliot's affections.'

'If you knew what I was assuming you could have corrected me.'

She sat down, reached for soft brown sugar to put into her coffee. She was conscious of so much more than the place where they both were, for the full moon had glided from behind the woolpacks to fill the landscape with an argent glow, and in the purple heavens too the Southern Cross was flaring, magnificent and somehow a little awesome in its magnitude.

'I didn't know, at the time, that you were assuming it was me. I can see it clearly now, and it explains why you were so strange, your attitude so bewildering.' She paused, having slight difficulty in articulating the next words but they came forth at length. 'You were wildly jealous of Elliot—both then and afterwards, when you saw him holding my hand. But although you denied being jealous it wasn't the truth. Scott,' she said rather breathlessly in conclusion, 'it so happens that I love you, too, so please don't deny it again, will you?' She felt she had been called upon to do all the talking, when it should have been Scott making the first confession of love. What did it matter, though?

He just looked at her for a long moment of silence and then,

'It so happens. . . . Can't you find a more romantic way of saying you love me?'

Her chin lifted.

'It's your turn,' she said, and at that he rose from his chair and Jane was gently brought to her feet.

'What a muddle it all was,' he said after a long while during which he made most passionate love to her, smothering her mouth with kisses, and her throat, and lower to where the delicate curves of her breasts were tantalisingly outlined beneath the tight-fitting bodice of her dress. His hands had not been idle, either, and Jane was aroused in a way that made her want to postpone all further talking for another time . . . preferably the following morning.

Scott, though, had regained his calm; she marvelled at his ability to do so. 'I suppose I was to blame for most of it,' he went on to admit. 'You see, my darling, that although I believed I felt nothing for you when we became engaged, I know now that you attracted me almost from the beginning. I couldn't bring myself to make a confession of love when I wasn't sure about your feelings for me. But that night, when we made love, I somehow felt convinced that you cared—'

'But the next morning you accused me of sleeping with a man I wasn't intending to marry,' Jane could not help reminding him.

'That was because of your own attitude,' he excused himself. 'Anyway, you knew darned well I didn't mean it, just as you didn't mean it when you said you wouldn't marry me if I was the last man on earth.'

'Did I say that, Scott?' Jane felt her cheeks become hot as the blood surged into them.

Scott gave her a playful tap.

'You know very well you did,' he admonished. 'I wasn't flattered.'

Jane laughed then and lifted her face, inviting his kiss. He obliged and for another long interval there was silence between them.

'My very dearly beloved. . . .' Scott's voice was hoarse and vibrant with passion. 'I love you so much . . . so very much. Why should I be so lucky?' He leant away and stared tenderly into her eyes. 'Can you tell me?'

'It's I who am lucky,' she said huskily. 'Oh, Scott, I never thought that anyone like you could love me!'

He gave her a little shake.

'Don't you ever talk like that,' he chided with mock severity. 'Why shouldn't I fall in love with you? You're beautiful, and sweet and desirable. . . .' Again his voice was a throaty bass inflection and Jane found herself swept helplessly into the vortex of his passion. She was quivering in every nerve cell, her heartbeats wild and swift.

'My own dear love,' she whispered, as with fumbling unsure fingers she unbuttoned his shirt so that she could slip her hand inside to experience the sweet pleasure of his warmth, his flesh beneath her touch. An intense yearning flowed into her, wild and sweet and precious. Time stood still and the primordial silence around them was complete. High above in the purple arc of the heavens the moon flared with a silver effulgence which lit the whole landscape to give it a ghostly aspect, and away in the mysterious distance the mountains were bathed in a gentle argent light. The dry river bed with its flanking gum trees; the cut-off—or billabong as it was called in Australia—these too were vividly illuminated, as were the gardens of the homestead and the trees which formed its boundaries.

'My love. . . .' Scott's breath was cool and clean against her temple. 'Shall we go in and make love?' He held her from him, his mouth twitching at her heightened colour. She tried to speak, wishing her pulses would quieten. 'You're shy, my sweet, but why? This won't be the first time, you know.'

She hesitated, not at all sure how she was to broach the subject which Scott would naturally not expect at a time like this. But he was in a mellow mood . . . and there was no time like the present.

'Scott. . . . Would you give me the particular wedding present I want?'

He looked amazed, as well he might.

'What on earth—?'

'The brumbie—er—do you consider it to be yours?'

'Of course.' His puzzlement was growing.

'But it should by rights belong to me, surely?'

'I brought him in.'

'Only because he was lame. You'd never have managed it otherwise.'

Scott frowned at her.

'Just what is all this about?' he wanted to know.

'I can't rest if he's to be in captivity,' she confessed. 'He's mine, really, but since you've claimed him I'm asking you to give him to me as a present.'

Scott's dark eyes narrowed. The hold on her arms slackened and she frowned on missing their strength and their warmth.

'So you can set him free, obviously?'

'That's right.'

'Someone else would attempt to catch him—'

'Not if he were my property. I believe that they would all respect the fact that he was your wedding present to me.' Her big eyes were wide and pleading. Scott, loving her to distraction, was at the same time unable to see himself setting free the superb animal whom every rancher for miles around had had visions of owning.

'This is a whim,' he said at last, hoping to convince her. 'He'll be as happy as Larry in a couple of months' time.'

'He'll die in captivity,' she pronounced emphatically. 'And there's another thing: yesterday I saw a mare and she had a new-born foal.'

'Well?'

'I guess they're his mate and his baby.'

Amusement touched the fine outline of Scott's lips, but Jane did not despair, because of the hint of tenderness there too, and because of the gentle way he reached out to take hold of her hand.

'You're very sweet,' he murmured softly, close to her throat. 'You're probably all wrong, and it isn't his mate and his foal—'

'The foal's his colour, exactly,' she broke swiftly to inform him.

'It is?' with interest. 'Then you might just be right in that guess of yours.'

She looked at him with pleading and a certain degree of trust and optimism.

'Then you'll do as I ask?'

He gave a deep sigh and it was some moments before he answered her.

'It would be one of the hardest things I've done in my life,' he asserted, and he shook his head as if he could not see himself acceding to her request. 'We often bring in brumbies, you know, and they soon become used to living on the station.'

'You say that, but you don't really know how they feel. Horses bred here are different; they haven't ever known anything else. But this one—' She spread her hands, aware that the brumbie's future was the paramount issue at this time, that she could never be happy seeing him harnessed, ridden by Scott even though, as Crystal had said, Scott would be kind to him. 'It's an important issue, Scott,' she said pleadingly. 'He's so proud and beautiful, and used to roaming these rangelands—they're his territory; he goes where he likes.'

'And no doubt enjoys the sport of evading his would-be capturers.' Scott's tone was crisp and a small frown knit his brow. Jane thought that he could be unmovable if he made a decision.

'No one has the right to capture him,' she said with a hint of impatience. 'Freedom's his birthright.'

'If I hadn't gone out there and brought him in for treatment he'd probably have died,' Scott couldn't help reminding her.

'He'd most likely prefer death to captivity.'

'Now you're being ridiculous.' Censure shaded his eyes.

'What you did was only right; animals should be helped if they're injured or ill.'

He looked down at her, noticing the quiver of her lips, the anxious expression in her eyes. He was still torn, for he had been complimenting himself on obtaining what so many others had been after for a very long time.

'Does it really mean so much to you, my dear?' he asked at last, bringing her to him and caressing her cheek. 'Are you sure you wouldn't like to have him here all the time, make friends with him, have him sire some lovely foals which our children could ride?'

She shook her head, blushing a little at his reference to children.

'His foals would grow up to be far too lively for children.'

'But at first—as soon as they are old enough to be saddled. . . .' His voice tapered off to silence as she shook her head again.

'Please give him to me for a wedding present,' she said again. 'I'll love you more than ever for that,' she added and he had to laugh. A resigned sigh soon followed and suddenly Jane's heart was light as all anxiety left her.

'You win,' he muttered almost to himself. She smiled in triumph but kept her head averted, resting her cheek against his chest. 'He can go.'

'No, I want him as a wedding present,' she insisted.

'Is it important?' That he was puzzled was obvious.

'Yes, it is, because, as I've already said, all the others who have wanted him will give up, respecting the fact that he's really my property, having been given to me as a wedding present from you.'

Another sigh.

'All right, if that's what'll make you happy.'

'Oh, but I love you!'

His gaze was one of grim amusement.

'Clever girl, you are telling yourself, aren't you? You can wind your husband around your little finger. Well, my poor disillusioned one, you can have another think! I might have given in to you this time but don't make a practice of this wheedling because it won't work. Understand?' He held her at arm's length and looked down at her with mock sternness. 'Well?'

She controlled the urge to laugh. And instead said meekly,

'Of course, dearest Scott, I understand. This is the one and only time I shall try to—er—wheedle, as you describe it.'

'You're asking for a shaking,' he warned when despite her control her lips began to twitch. 'But instead I think I shall kiss you—' And suddenly she was swept into his arms, her breasts flattened against the iron hardness of his chest. He tilted her face, made her meet his gaze for a long, long moment before, bending his head, he took possession of her lips. She felt the full length of her body pressed against the muscled tautness of his frame as he crushed her to him, felt the solidity of his hipbone, the pure masculine strength of his thighs, the pressure of hands against the soft curves of her lower body as he curled his fingers to take their shape. Nerve-ends became alive, pulses raced, and her heart was pounding wildly against her ribcage. Sensuous arousal was controlling her senses, urging her to arch against him, as if she would meld her body inseparably with his. She strained, helped by the deliberate pressure and temptation of his hands as they slid beneath her clothing to caress her flesh. She twined her arms about his neck, experimenting with feather-light caresses on his nape and the vulnerable places behind his ears, his responsive quivers exciting her to a state of sheer exhilaration and expectancy. Rapture affected her whole body when his mouth, moist and possessive, trailed from her lips to her throat where the sensitive hollow drew and held it for a long moment before it found her breast. A spasm darted through her, and, shaken and panting, she whispered huskily,

'Scott . . . you . . . you want to go in. . . .'

'We both want to go in,' he uttered with a low and throaty little laugh. 'We must be very quiet, though. . . .' Lifting her tenderly into his arms he moved to the window, entered the room and with smooth fluid movements carried her through and up the stairs. A deep, erotic longing enveloped her, swamping all thought but the primordial one of complete surrender and fulfillment.

He stood her on her feet after entering her bedroom, and their eyes met and held in loving, melting moments before, with tender hands, he removed her dress and then the lacy underskirt that was in effect part of it. Colour, delicate and peach-bloomed, filtered into her cheeks and her eyes were shy and lowered, tenderly shaded by long curling lashes. She stood before him in all the glory of youth, her hair a halo of gleaming silk about shoulders that sloped divinely, naked shoulders white and smooth beneath the hands that caressed them. A rapturous sensation of belonging to someone, body and soul, swept like a warm shower over her and the smile she gave him was tender and loving. With a muffled exclamation he caught her to him, sliding his eager hands into a tiny covering and removing it. The bra came away and she was naked, no longer shy because of her awakened desires and the fevered longing for his body claiming hers in the final moment of surrender.

'How beautiful you are!' His mouth was hard against her lips, sensuous and moist and dominantly mobile so that she was forced to part her lips, quivering with sweet rapture at the feel of his rough tongue caressing hers. He lifted her and laid her on the cover of the bed, switched off the main light, leaving only a romantic glow from a single bed lamp with its peach-coloured shade. She closed her eyes, and when she opened them again he was getting onto the bed beside her, naked and muscled and virile. A shudder passed through her when he took her cool body in his arms, his mouth moving to one firm high breast and resting there, and she felt the caress of his tongue on the nipple.

The sheer ache of longing brought her body arching in fevered haste, and her arms wound themselves about his neck. She thrilled to the warmth of his nakedness, to the strength of his embrace, to the knowledge of his hard virility that told her of his urgent need of her. Her skin was on fire from the heat of his passion, a passion that was rising with full, primitive fierceness as his hands moulded themselves to the shape of her curves . . . and then he was caressing secret places, murmuring endearments through ragged, uneven breathing.

'My darling . . . my wife. . . .'

She clung to him in eager response as his body began to move in rhythm, and parted her legs, trembling with the ecstasy of his mastery as he took her with movements as savage as they were tender. Her mind was dazed by the rapture that shuddered through her over and over again as Scott's moment of fulfillment drew ever closer . . . until that moment when the whole world around them exploded and they were soaring into the clouds, where heaven was. . . .

Long, long moments later Scott said, his voice husky with tiredness,

'You'll marry me soon, my darling? I did say a week, you know.'

'Four days have gone already.' Jane yawned and snuggled close against his chest.

'That leaves three. Plenty of time.'

'All right, if you want that kind of wedding. I daresay I'll find something that'll suffice in my scanty wardrobe—' A slap on the behind brought her words to an abrupt stop as Jane uttered a little protesting, 'Oh!'

'So how long do you want?'

'The dress—shall I have to go into town to get it made?'

'Perhaps—yes, I suppose so.'

'I'll be as quick as I can,' she promised. And then as the idea occurred to her, 'Everyone is going to be so surprised because they all suspect our engagement's only a sham.'

'Well, they're soon going to learn otherwise.' Scott spread a hard leg across her body. 'I suppose it can't be done in less than a week seeing that invitations have to be sent out.'

'A week! Oh, Scott, really! You seem to forget that I have parents. I couldn't get married without letting them know.'

'Your parents. . . . They ought to be here for the wedding,' he conceded and her heart leapt at the possibility. 'Yes, we can't rush it too much.' His pronouncement came with obvious reluctance but it was firm. 'You hear from them regularly?'

'Of course.' She paused a moment and then, 'In their last letter they gave me some news that I'd been waiting for.'

'Yes?' Scott was suddenly bored with what they were saying and with a faint smile Jane realised he was intending to make love to her again.

'You once asked me why I came here.'

'I'm glad you did.' A small pause ensued. 'Why did you come?'

'Because I was falling in love with the fiancé of my friend.'

'What!' He was wide awake all at once.

'I soon knew it was nothing—because I was falling in love with the Boss of Jacana Downs and this time it was real. However, this news: Mother's written to say that Paddy and Mary were married earlier this month and are now honeymooning in Scotland. Isn't that wonderful news?'

'If you say so,' murmured Scott, plainly wanting to dismiss the subject. 'Darling, do you realise that in a short while I've to get up off this bed and leave you?'

'Oh. . . .'

'So don't let us waste any more time on things which we can talk about in the morning.' His lips found hers in a long and passionate kiss. 'And because I've to leave you is a very important reason for getting married just as soon as possible, so you must write to your parents tomorrow and tell them to get the first plane out.'

A low laugh escaped her. How like him, the arrogant Boss of Jacana Downs, to think he could order her parents about in the same way that he ordered his fiancée about!

She said with a quiver of amusement,

'I'll do my best, darling. . . .' But she got no further, because her words were masterfully silenced by the sensuous pressure of her lover's mouth.

Silhouette Romance

IT'S YOUR OWN SPECIAL TIME

Contemporary romances for today's women.
Each month, six very special love stories will be yours
from SILHOUETTE. Look for them wherever books are sold
or order now from the coupon below.

$1.50 each

Hampson	☐ 1	☐ 4	☐ 16	☐ 27	Browning	☐ 12	☐ 38	☐ 53	☐ 73
	☐ 28	☐ 52	☐ 94			☐ 93			
Stanford	☐ 6	☐ 25	☐ 35	☐ 46	Michaels	☐ 15	☐ 32	☐ 61	☐ 87
	☐ 58	☐ 88			John	☐ 17	☐ 34	☐ 57	☐ 85
Hastings	☐ 13	☐ 26			Beckman	☐ 8	☐ 37	☐ 54	☐ 96
Vitek	☐ 33	☐ 47	☐ 84		Wisdom	☐ 49	☐ 95		
Wildman	☐ 29	☐ 48			Halston	☐ 62	☐ 83		

☐ 5 Goforth	☐ 22 Stephens	☐ 50 Scott	☐ 81 Roberts
☐ 7 Lewis	☐ 23 Edwards	☐ 55 Ladame	☐ 82 Dailey
☐ 9 Wilson	☐ 24 Healy	☐ 56 Trent	☐ 86 Adams
☐ 10 Caine	☐ 30 Dixon	☐ 59 Vernon	☐ 89 James
☐ 11 Vernon	☐ 31 Halldorson	☐ 60 Hill	☐ 90 Major
☐ 14 Oliver	☐ 36 McKay	☐ 63 Brent	☐ 92 McKay
☐ 19 Thornton	☐ 39 Sinclair	☐ 71 Ripy	☐ 97 Clay
☐ 20 Fulford	☐ 43 Robb	☐ 76 Hardy	☐ 98 St. George
☐ 21 Richards	☐ 45 Carroll	☐ 78 Oliver	☐ 99 Camp

$1.75 each

Stanford	☐ 100	☐ 112	☐ 131		Browning	☐ 113	☐ 142	☐ 164	☐ 172
Hardy	☐ 101	☐ 130	☐ 184		Michaels	☐ 114	☐ 146		
Cork	☐ 103	☐ 148	☐ 188		Beckman	☐ 124	☐ 154	☐ 179	
Vitek	☐ 104	☐ 139	☐ 157	☐ 176	Roberts	☐ 127	☐ 143	☐ 163	☐ 180
Dailey	☐ 106	☐ 118	☐ 153	☐ 177	Trent	☐ 110	☐ 161	☐ 193	
	☐ 195				Wisdom	☐ 132	☐ 166		
Bright	☐ 107	☐ 125			Hunter	☐ 137	☐ 167		
Hampson	☐ 108	☐ 119	☐ 128	☐ 136	Scott	☐ 117	☐ 169	☐ 187	
	☐ 147	☐ 151	☐ 155	☐ 160	Sinclair	☐ 123	☐ 174		
	☐ 178	☐ 185	☐ 190		John	☐ 115	☐ 192		

Silhouette Romance

Coming next month from
Silhouette Romances

Sunset in Paradise by Carole Halston

When Aunt Liz sold their house to the wealthy and handsome Jonathan Talbot, Fran's carefree days in Key West seemed numbered . . . until she made herself part of the deal.

Trail Of The Unicorn by Cathryn LaDame

Working for her uncle at the Unicorn Society Institute was very different from working under arrogant Thane Fraser out in the field, where Lesley knew she'd have to fight to prove her ability.

Flight Of Fancy by Laura Eden

Lisa Ashton wanted only two things in life and neither included the devastatingly handsome Serge Devereaux . . . until he offered her the job she wanted with his aviation firm!

Greek Idyll by Jade Walters

Rosalie Darrien wanted to teach the wealthy Louis Alexander that a pretty girl was more than a mere toy to be played with—but in the process she fell under his spell.

Yesterday's Promise by Karen Young

Late hours at a Boston engineering firm left Julie Dunaway no time for love until the dynamic new consultant they hired turned out to be her estranged husband.

Separate Cabins by Janet Dailey

When Gardiner MacKinley met Rachel MacKinley aboard the Mexican Riviera cruise, he wanted to share more than just a last name, but could Rachel believe his tender vows for the future?

6 brand new
Silhouette Special Editions
yours for 15 days–Free!

For the reader who wants more…more story…more detail and description…more realism…and more romance…in paperback originals, 1/3 longer than our regular Silhouette Romances. Love lingers longer in new Silhouette Special Editions. Love weaves an intricate, provocative path in a third more pages than you have just enjoyed. It is love as you have always wanted it to be—and more —intriguingly depicted by your favorite Silhouette authors in the inimitable Silhouette style.

15-Day Free Trial Offer

We will send you 6 new Silhouette Special Editions to keep for 15 days absolutely free! If you decide not to keep them, send them back to us, you pay nothing. But if you enjoy them as much as we think you will, keep them and pay the invoice enclosed with your trial shipment. You will then automatically become a member of the Special Edition Book Club and receive 6 more romances every month. There is no minimum number of books to buy and you can cancel at any time.

- - - - **FREE CHARTER MEMBERSHIP COUPON** - - -

 Silhouette Special Editions, Dept. SESB-1M
120 Brighton Road, Clifton, NJ 07012

Please send me 6 Silhouette Special Editions to keep for 15 days, absolutely free. I understand I am not obligated to join the Silhouette Special Editions Book Club unless I decide to keep them.

Name _____

Address _____

City _____

State_____ Zip _____

This offer expires July 31, 1983

READERS' COMMENTS ON SILHOUETTE ROMANCES:

"I would like to congratulate you on the most wonderful books I've had the pleasure of reading. They are a tremendous joy to those of us who have yet to meet the man of our dreams. From reading your books I quite truly believe that he will someday appear before me like a prince!"

—L.L.*, Hollandale, MS

"Your books are great, wholesome fiction, always with an upbeat, happy ending. Thank you."

—M.D., Massena, NY

"My boyfriend always teases me about Silhouette Books. He asks me, how's my love life and naturally I say terrific, but I tell him that there is always room for a little more romance from Silhouette."

—F.N., Ontario, Canada

"I would like to sincerely express my gratitude to you and your staff for bringing the pleasure of your publications to my attention. Your books are well written, mature and very contemporary."

—D.D., Staten Island, NY

*names available on request